¶ wish
that all
fighting over
religion, colour &
creed would stop & we
embraced differences ¶ I wish
for continued regeneration and
vibrancy so everyone can achieve their
potential in an healthy, artistic, modern
environmetn ¶ I wish all citizens have the potential to
live happily in solidarity removing poverty and injustic
Loving people ¶ I wish our elderly people to feel respe
valued, our children to feel good about living well, havi
and education. I want to stop disruption of bigotry and
society of citizens committed to caring for neighbours, env
all our citizens are enabled to fulfil their potential and that our c
caring and empowered. I wish the city's economy to prosper and for
place to visit to grow ¶ I wish that everyone of every age thinks about the c
make our city the envy of the world - neighbourliness and pride ¶ My wish is fo
can all be proud of - citizens care for one another and are tolerant ¶ My wish fs for G
the centre fo the universe, safe, nice houses for everyone ¶ My fervent wish is to see Glasg
modern, 21st century city fit for purpose to serve the citizens of Glasgow in quality of life. Econo
happy and confident city ¶ I wish the regeneration of the East End complete so it is cleaner with a wel
complex ¶ To have a poverty-free city. To instil pride once again. A city where we welcome all religions, c
society. Jobs for our young. Independent Scotland and Glasgow ¶ For a city free from the evils of racism and sec
everyone that lives and works here treats all others with dignity and respect. No to racism, bigotry, fascism & nationa
Glaswegians could become more conscious of the image they project of our city when they drop litter on our streets.
more litter bins ¶ I wish the North of Glasgow to be filled with good housing and work places. All children to have a g ite
style ¶ I wish for a Glasgow that can promote peace and understanding throughout the world and here in the city ¶ I wish t nt city
where local communities are recognised and supported in contributing to the success of the city. I wish for a city free of poverty a t to be
recognised for the ability of its people, its humour and its great social and cultural diversity ¶ I wish good health to all the residents in G y to all her
citizens ¶ I wish that everyone in Glasgow has the same opportunities as others, for less anti-social behaviour and more community spirit, ho ick Thistle
win the SPL and Scottish Cup ¶ More money spent on houses and jobs in the city ¶ I like the museum, I wish it was bigger ¶ To be taken seriously he olden
days and to keep the streets cleaner ¶ I wish that limousines weren't so expensive! ¶ I wish for a full time visitor assistant's post at Kelvingrove or any mu aded ¶ I
wish you could go into stuff and places ¶ I wish for a new house and a cat and a horse ¶ I wish for lots and lots of pets ¶ I wish that you could eat all the ice c at ¶ I
wish my brother would be better and walk and see ¶ I wish my friend could stay over at my house all the time ¶ I wish I had a cute dog ¶ I wish we had moving pav a cute
baby brother ¶ I wish I had a rabbit ¶ I wish I could drive ¶ I wish I had the Rangers strip and top ¶ I wish Glasgow would help the homeless and give working class peop life
instead of paying up for those who get everything for nothing and nursery charges should be true ¶ I wish Glasgow University would be demolished to make room for the one tr ow,
Strathclyde! ¶ I wish for the improvement of local high streets in deprived areas & that middle class people moving into areas like the Govan and the Gorbals would use local shops ¶ the
communities of Glasgow are safe places to live, work and visit ¶ I wish that Glasgow strives to be cleaner, safer and a happy place to live ¶ I wish that all the citizens of Glasgow have the sa nity to
reach their full potential regardless of their background, wealth, upbringing etc. ¶ I wish that all children in Glasgow are able to enjoy their childhood and grow up in a safe and happy environme wish
that Glasgow was clean and had no vehicles apart from bicycles in the city center ¶ I wish that there would be happiness and peace among citizens, I wish that the coming generations will utilise their full
potential and benefit us all! ¶ I wish that Glasgow would be pollutionless and safe ¶ I wish that Glasgow will continue to build its future by investing in young people, who are the future ¶ I wish that
Glasgow will continue to keep its appeal for toursits to help the economy get morejobs for people ¶ I wish for safe green spaces, running water and room for children to grow up happy and free, and able to
reach their potential in life. I wish for happiness, freedom, love and joy ¶ I wish for an end to the bigoed poisen that has contaminated this city for generations, and that more people would support Partick
Thistle ¶ I wish that Glasgow come to terms with its own contradictions — contradictions of race, religion, wealth...and its own contradiction as the poor man of Europe. Its the richest city i've ever known ¶
I wish we could get rid of all the ugly people - Maybe to Edinburgh ¶ I wish that people outside of Glasgow knew what a great city it is, and that it lost its reputation as a rough city as its no worse than
anywhere else ¶ I wish for every person in Glasgow to never feel ashamed of their talents, abilities or money, and for no person to ever live solely for another ¶ I wish Glasgow a happy healthy and
prosperous future — welcoming our visitors and caring for those in need. Let Glasgow flourish ¶ I wish Glasgow could dispose of the Neds, Chavs, Jokey and the like. Would be an even better place without
em ¶ I wish for peace among all the people on earth and for us all to care for the earth and treat the earth tenderly, and each other as well. Namaste ¶ A Ned-free Glasgow! — I wish that Glaswegians
would get some civic pride. We have a great city, its just a pity that all the manky little louts and and neds spoil it for the rest of us ¶ I wish to win the lotto jackpot this weekend ¶ I wish for a good and
happy future for my kids and myself ¶ I wish the world would be a happy and peaceful place and for me and my family to have a great life ¶ Everyone — Today, 2006 to make changes in their lives to save
our planet! Cars, litter, fumes, chemicals. 2020 to be clean. ¶ I wish I wasn't fat and ugly, cos i am. But i wish i Wasn't so i could have more m8s ¶ Having had an excellent night with a Glasgow based
company I would express my gratitude to Glasgow for the clear culture and standing I have enjoyed ¶ I wish the establishment would self distruct and allow honest, working folk to the country ¶ I hope this
girls (Amy Hughes) wish comes true, and that Chelsea win the league next year 3rd time in a row. Ollie wishes good health for all his family and friends. ¶ I wish to lose weight this year and to win a wee bet
on the lottery. And peacce on earth for all ¶ I wish to lose weight and be happy and content. Let the world be happy, no fighting. Love to my husband Craig ¶ I want to make my wife happy and be content
to share my life with her forever ¶ I want to live the rest of my life with Jean my wife of almost 38 years. I also wish for peace in the world!! ¶ I want to be with my lovely husband 'till the day i die, and
make him the happiest man alive, because he deserves it so much ¶ Glasgow is fabulous — Long may it flourish ¶ Life Love and Happiness ¶ I wish for love, laughter, happiness, good wealth for
myself, family and friends. And if i'm really lucky some sunshine ¶ I wish 4 a day off ¶ Health Wealth and Happiness, and a big pay rise ¶ I wish i was 14! — and my sister stopped pulling
my hair ¶ Peace on Earth ¶ I wish i could read people's minds ¶ I wish i could get an iPod. And be able to fly. England win the world cup ¶ I wish for a better and more tolerant world
¶ I wish i didn't spend my time making frivolous wishes ¶ I wish the Tower would open and i wish for smoking ban to be lifted and for secutrity to get a pay rise ¶ I wish for a
tolerant world toward all peoples ¶ A better life for my two grandchildren and to live in a safe and healthy world ¶ I wish I could go for Download ¶ I wish for health, love,
happiness for me and my family and if we are lucky maybe wealth too. I wish for a cure for cancer and all other life threatening illness. ¶ I wish to be a footballer for AC
Milan¶ To come first in the Olympics ¶ For fun and sun for everyone ¶ I wish for a cure for Parkinson's Disease, a more tolerant society and wealth, prosperity and
happiness for all my family, especially my nana and pape, Khala's, Mamos, and Waseme, and my Mum and Sister ¶ Jest tu super ¶ I wish I was 26 ¶ I wish
their would be peace in the world and all illnesses had a cure. I wish my family and friends could have a great and healthy, long, happy life! ¶ I wish my
girlfriend woud shut up sometimes ¶ I wish I was 20 again! ¶ I wish my mum would stop moaning at me ¶ I wish my dad didn't eat all my pies ¶ I
wish I could afford a bra for my man boobs! ¶ I wish my husband Drew would stop raiding the fridge and steeling my daughter Nicola's
muffins - it's costing me a bloody fortune! ¶ I wish my boyfriend Aders would make lots of money and spend it on me! Ps. In particular
I'd like a pony! ¶ I wish a cure for herpes is found within the next 5 years and to not be selfish. HIV as well. ¶ I wish for an endless
supply of chocolate, yum ¶ I wish my mum would remember my socks with my clean clothes when she sens me up to my
grans ¶ I want to be a footballer ¶ In 2020 I wish to be a footballer for rangers ¶ I wish there was a basketball club in
my area!!!!! ¶ I want to make a million ¶ I want to be rich ¶ Happy life, healthy life, sunny life ¶ For Laurens love
¶ To never be to old! ¶ I wish for a cure for cystic fibrosis ¶ To win the lottery ¶. To still be loved by Susie ¶
To grow old with Alan N have a healthy happy family. And to achieve everything I want. ¶ To go far in
life, do well at work and someone to love me ¶ I wish that Glasgow becomes a safe, clean and
drug-free city ¶ I wish there was a permanent cure for cancer ¶ I wish for world peace, an
end to poverty, an end to pollution, and for Glasgow to be a safe and friendly city like it
was many years ago ¶ I wish that people would realise that we are all people
from one planet and should not be divided by colour, race or religion ¶ I
wish everyone in the world would be nicer to each other that way we
could live in a much happier planet ¶ I hope and wish girls
would stop phoning me 24/7 ¶ I wish for a step-change in
Glasgow's international competitiveness ¶ I would
like to see less sectarianism ¶ I wish to see an
abolition of the welfare state, thus providing
more money for housing, hospitals,
schools, policing,etc ¶ I wish to
see Glasgow take a more
influential role in
European affairs

—

THE DREAMING CITY

AND
THE POWER
OF MASS
IMAGINATION

—

DEMOS

First published in 2007 by Demos
© Demos
Some rights reserved. See page 237
ISBN 978-1-84180-186-5
Copy edited by Susannah Wight
Typeset‡ and designed by Åbäke in London
Printed by Aldgate Press, London
    For further information and subscription
    please contact:
        Demos
        Magdalen House
        136 Tooley Street
        London SE1 2TU
        T: 0845 458 5949
        e: hello@demos.co.uk
        www.demos.co.uk

‡ A note from the designers: This book is set in Mockintosh and Optima. The latter is a family designed in the 1950s by Herman Zapf. According to its creator, it is a an alphabet design between a Roman and a sans-serif. A successful hybrid for the fans and merely a compromise for its detractors. In this present case, we chose it because of our total inability to predict whether serif or sans-serif will be the taste of 2020.

Endpapers: Wishes for Glasgow in 2020. See page 170

THE DREAMING CITY

GLASGOW 2020 AND THE POWER OF MASS IMAGINATION

CONTENTS

St Mungo's Mirrorball
— Jim Carruth

Does not spin the way you'd like
It jigs between pitch dark and light
It staggers with drink, swaggers with balls
Swoops like starlings over Barras stalls
Sends shipyard shadows on tenement walls
It's a high rise sway, It's a smile in the rain
It's a magic sparkle on the Provost's chain
Like the clockwork orange beneath the ground
It can change direction go both ways round
March back in time to drums and flutes
Past uni students and beggars in suits
And with every turn a revelation
Through the smoke of Central station
Banks are bistros, churches are flats
Their basements are rising damp and rats
Around each corner meet the past
A deep fried life not meant to last
The capital of heart attacks
This Mirrorball is full of cracks
Tamson's bairns upon each face
Split the clouds in the dear green place

Glasgow's love's no more than this
Both Valentine's heart and painful kiss
Clumsy moves end nights on the piss
Knox scowls down from the Necropolis
While beneath this ball Glasgow swings
With bass rhythms and cathedral rings
Franz Ferdinand and Barrowland kings
Country and western under angel wings
   John Maclean and his George Square noise
   Charms Gregory's Girl and the Glasgow Boys
Lord Kelvin birls around Rab Haw
As they dance doon the Broomielaw
Soon sweating up his Second law
   Do the Hogback, the Rennie Mack
   Over cappuccinos hear the craic
   Enlightenment its coming back
Offering up its gifts for all
Glorious Mungo's mirrorball
   It does not spin the way you'd like
   It shudders forward full of life.

ACKNOWLEDGEMENTS.

Just over two years ago Demos published Scotland 2020[1] — the conclusion of the project of the same name. This made the case for the importance of story in imagining the future. The inspiration for Glasgow 2020 came out of this. We wanted to test the appeal of story with a much larger audience and gauge their appetite for futures literacy and mass imagination. We wanted to do this at the level of a city: Scotland's largest city, Glasgow.

We have to say that we are proud of this project — proud of the enthusiasm, passion and wisdom of the people who contributed to it, the time and energy they gave to it, and the seriousness and reflection alongside the humour and fun. Glasgow 2020 was a unique and unusual project, far removed from the conventional concerns of the world of think tanks. More importantly, it was a unique project in the world — the first ever attempt anywhere to aspire to the re-imagination of a city through the idea of story.

A project as ambitious and unconventional as this has many collaborators and it would be impossible to thank everyone who contributed to and supported the project. First, to the people of Glasgow and the other cities across the world with whom we collaborated — a humble thank you. This project would not have been possible without your input, energy, goodwill and enthusiasm.

Second, to the storytellers and storycreators who were involved in Glasgow 2020. This has been one of the defining elements of the project, and a selection of

the stories of the future is gathered in this volume.
To everyone who was inspired to take pen to paper
and let loose their creative imagination — whether
at one of our events or as a result of one of our
competitions — thank you.

Third, thank you to the more than 2000 people
who made a wish for Glasgow. Many thanks to the
teachers who spread the wish campaign to schools,
all the organisations who hosted freepost wishcards
and finally to Mark Beever, for binding the wishbook
— an indestructible totem that will live for centuries!

Fourth, we would like to thank the project partners
who made Glasgow 2020 and to also highlight that
none asked to have any veto or final say on any of our
findings or outputs. A sincere thanks to Glasgow City
Council, Scottish Enterprise Glasgow, Glasgow Housing
Association, Glasgow Centre for Population Health,
Communities Scotland, Greater Glasgow and Clyde NHS
Board, Firstgroup, Strathclyde Police, Strathclyde Fire
and Rescue, Glasgow University, Glasgow Caledonian
University, Glasgow School of Art, Royal Scottish
Academy of Music and Drama, Scottish Arts Council,
VisitScotland, Scottish Executive National Programme
for Mental Health and Well-Being, Glasgow Anti-Racist
Alliance, Scotland UnLtd and the *Evening Times*. This
group contains nearly every single significant public
agency in the city — all of which contributed and
engaged with the project.

Finally, to the many individuals and organisations
who picked up Glasgow 2020 and ran with it: to the
Castlemilk Youth Project who produced their own
Glasgow 2020 DVD; to some of the hairdressers at

DLC Hair Salon who sparked a national (and indeed international) debate about the power of hairdressers; to everyone who braved the rain to move their office to *The Pride of the Clyde* boat in October 2005 and to the 'Creative Carriage' team facilitated by the Scottish Adult Learning Partnership for running mobile mass-imagination on the Glasgow – Edinburgh trains.
To those and many more we are grateful that you chose to contribute to this project and make it exciting and unpredictable.

A project of the scale and ambition of Glasgow 2020 would not have been possible without the dedication of a number of people who worked with us throughout the whole process. John Daly and Keith Hunter of 101 Dimensions facilitated many of our events with passion and integrity. Jenny Hamill and Diane Hutchison of Oyster Arts assisted in the logistics of numerous activities with grace. Jenny gained both a husband and a son during the project — we would like to thank her especially for her commitment to the project. Sharon Halliday and Craig Jardine of Infinite Eye designed and modified the project website and were responsible for our fabulous Glasgow 2020 logo.

Glasgow 2020 inspired a wide range of people to contribute time and effort, enthusiasm and ideas. Pre-project, Ken Wardrop, then of Scottish Enterprise Glasgow, Carol Tannahill, of Glasgow Centre for Population Health, and Jim McCormick, of Scottish Council Foundation, gave their thoughts and insights to aiding the initial project proposal.

Through the course of the project we were blessed by the valuable advice of many wonderful people. Jean Cameron of The Arts Practice was a passionate and committed advocate of this project as she is of the art she believes in and coined the idea 'assemblies of hope.' Jacqueline Whymark of the Scottish Adult Learning Partnership helped to make the 'Creative Carriage' a wonderful experience for everyone involved. Liz Gardner of Fablevision and Russell McClarty, then the Church of Scotland minister at St Paul's Church, were enthusiastic believers in the idea of story. Karen Cunningham, Head of Libraries, Culture and Sport Glasgow, and Bridget McConnell, Chief Executive of Culture and Sport Glasgow, supported this project through the Glasgow City Council. Phil Hanlon, Department of Public Health, Glasgow University, provided enthusiasm and numerous provocations. A big thank you also to David Leask, formerly of the *Evening Times*, and now of the *Herald*; Russell Leadbetter, of the *Evening Times*, and author of two of the best-selling books on Glasgow in recent years; and Charles McGhee and Janette Harkess, formerly editor and deputy editor of the *Evening Times* and now of the *Herald*, for the time and passion you showed with Glasgow 2020.

Glasgow 2020 was a learning experience for all of us. Many staff at Demos gave support from the cerebral to archiving and analysing the masses of materials (including lots of Post-it notes). We would like to thank specifically the interns Nasser Abourahme, Amanda Cecil, Chung Hey-Wan, Nayan Parekh, Amy Horton and Faton Shabi who worked voluntarily to support the project; Sam Hinton-Smith, Eddie Gibb, Julia Huber and Peter Harrington who provided communications support; Alison Harvie for her support in administering the project and in particular, Tom Bentley in the initial stages, and Joost Beunderman, John Holden and John Craig subsequently for their valuable insights. A last word and thought should go to Rosie Ilett who oversaw the last stage of checking references and proofing the whole document. All web references were checked in April 2007.

This book has been brilliantly designed by Åbäke, and copyedited by Susannah Wight. We would also like to thank Sefi Amir at Design Heroine for her work designing and dressing the space at the Big Dream event in the Kelvingrove Art Gallery and Museum.

We have all been changed by this experience. For a start we are all a bit older and maybe a bit wiser. We have lived with Glasgow 2020 for a long time and its unfolding tapestry has been part of our lives. We can honestly say that Glasgow 2020 was a humbling experience, offering the opportunity of meeting, listening and speaking to so many different people share their hopes and dreams.

This book is dedicated to the people of Glasgow who created it. We hope you see the city of the future in it and find it a useful road map to get there. We would like to be part of that journey.

Gerry Hassan — gerry.hassan@virgin.net
Melissa Mean — melissa.mean@demos.co.uk
Charlie Tims — charlie.tims@demos.co.uk

April 2007

PART 1

INTRO - DUCTION

' Stadtluft macht frei' — *City air makes you free*
Old German proverb[2]

This book maps the story of our cities — the places they are now and the places people hope they will become in the future. It is told through the experience of one city — Glasgow — where over the course of 18 months Demos facilitated an experiment to open up the city's future to the mass imagination of its citizens. What people created has resonance and learning not only for Glasgow, but for cities elsewhere and for anyone who is concerned with how we shape our shared futures.

Glasgow is a city which has experienced constant change and adaptation from its period as an 'imperial city', as the Second City of Empire and the Athens of the North, to its latter day reinvention as the City of Culture and Second City of Shopping. This is a city with pull, buzz, excitement, and a sense of style and its own importance. It has a potent international reach and influence. There are nearly two dozen towns and cities around the world named after Glasgow, following the trade threads of Empire — from Jamaica to Montana and even a Glasgow on the moon.[3] The Glasgow character has been much written about by people studying the city from within and outwith, some to praise it, and others to condemn it.

There is also the Glasgow with historic and deep inequalities, a city of sharp divisions in income, employment, life chances, lifestyle and health. In these relatively good times for the majority in Scotland and the UK, many of these inequalities have grown wider.[4]

JANUARY 2020

MO	TU	WE	TH	FR	SA	SU
		1	2	3	4	5
6	7	8	9	10	11	12
13	14	15	16	17	18	19
20	21	22	23	24	25	26
27	28	29	30	31		

This is a place whose past experience and contemporary tensions and possibilities offer a rich setting within which to examine the questions and dilemmas the modern city faces. Glasgow has shown a remarkable capacity for civic leadership and pride, past innovation and reinvention, and therefore makes a compelling site to ask what might come next in our urban futures.

The Glasgow 2020 project started out to:

develop a whole-city project:
engaging Glasgow's many different communities of place, interest and identity as well as civic and public institutions in a shared project.

FEBRUARY 2020

MO	TU	WE	TH	FR	SA	SU
					1	2
3	4	5	6	7	8	9
10	11	12	13	14	15	16
17	18	19	20	21	22	23
24	25	26	27	28	29	

develop a project that was not just about Glasgow but about cities more widely:
using activities in Glasgow to develop a wider set of conversations in other cities, enabling the sharing and contrasting of experiences and to test what is specific to Glasgow and what are common trends and findings.

to support the development of futures literacy:
exploring how people can act now to influence the future.

to design and test a process of mass imagination:
encouraging a critical mass of the population to reflect, imagine and create different futures.

Over the course of the project a wide range of activities took place, including:

MARCH 2020

MO	TU	WE	TH	FR	SA	SU
						1
2	3	4	5	6	7	8
9	10	11	12	13	14	15
16	17	18	19	20	21	22
23	24	25	26	27	28	29
30	31					

• 38 events across Glasgow and in Gothenburg, Helsinki and Stockholm, which ranged from intimate story creation workshops to large events that attracted hundreds of people.

• Using the public spaces of the city to help spark a public conversation, including: using the Glasgow – Edinburgh train service for a series of 'Creative Carriage' discussions; taking over the 'The Pride of the Clyde' and turning the boat into a floating open office for a day; and using the Kelvingrove Museum for a futures festival called the 'The Big Dream'.

• A 'Make a Wish for Glasgow' campaign, with a giant wish book touring the city collecting people's wishes and an invitation to all the six-year-olds in Glasgow to make a wish — over 1000 of them did so.

APRIL 2020

MO	TU	WE	TH	FR	SA	SU
		1	2	3	4	5
6	7	8	9	10	11	12
13	14	15	16	17	18	19
20	21	22	23	24	25	26
27	28	29	30			

•   Over 5000 people coming to events or directly submitting material and ideas — a figure which represents nearly 1 per cent of Glasgow's population. An even wider audience was reached through the website and media campaign with the city's main paper, the *Evening Times*.

A core set of propositions guided the philosophy, design and execution of the project.

The first step to a better future is imagining one: Thinking about the future is not something that can be left to futurologists or experts inside big institutions. Instead it needs to be open, participative and democratic. The idea of futures literacy means thinking imaginatively about the future but also being

MAY 2020

MO	TU	WE	TH	FR	SA	SU
				1	2	3
4	5	6	7	8	9	10
11	12	13	14	15	16	17
18	19	20	21	22	23	24
25	26	27	28	29	30	31

able to act in the present. By building up people's capacity and confidence to think about the future, futures literacy helps us challenge our everyday assumptions and leads to better decision-making. Becoming a futures-literate city means connecting individual and collective aspirations for the future at a scale and within contexts that people find meaningful and can participate in practically — in neighbourhoods, public spaces and public conversations.

'The official future' is increasingly problematic and disconnected from people:
A critical problem which contemporary cities face is that they have become dominated by institutions which

JUNE 2020

MO	TU	WE	TH	FR	SA	SU
1	2	3	4	5	6	7
8	9	10	11	12	13	14
15	16	17	18	19	20	21
22	23	24	25	26	27	28
29	30					

articulate an idea of the official future, leaving little room for people's everyday aspirations and creativity. This has led to a serious disconnect between the public and the institutions of urban governance with many people left feeling that the future is something that has already been decided, rather than something which is owned and co-created by everyone.

Urban policy and governance have become closed:
The space for innovation in urban governance, planning and design is debilitatingly narrow.
The dominant formula of city-boosterism and culture-led regeneration is increasingly spent.
Meanwhile the language of localism and devolution has yet to decisively open up any real freedom for civic

JULY 2020

MO	TU	WE	TH	FR	SA	SU
		1	2	3	4	5
6	7	8	9	10	11	12
13	14	15	16	17	18	19
20	21	22	23	24	25	26
27	28	29	30	31		

urban entrepreneurship. The result is a growing mismatch between the kind of cities people want and what cities are able to offer. This means there is a real danger that the current resurgence of cities will prove cyclical and short-lived rather than structural and sustained.

The stories we tell matter:
The stories that we tell matter because they indicate how we see the world, and whether we believe we have the power and capacity to shape it for the better. Stories are one of the main ways that we make sense of the world, and understand and interpret our lives and experiences. Stories and engaging people's imagination are potentially a powerful way to open up the futures of cities in democratic and creative ways.

AUGUST 2020

MO	TU	WE	TH	FR	SA	SU
					1	2
3	4	5	6	7	8	9
10	11	12	13	14	15	16
17	18	19	20	21	22	23
24	25	2	27	28	29	30
31						

Demos set out to test these propositions in Glasgow. Using storytelling and other tools to create a new mental map of Glasgow, the aim was to surface some new shared stories about the future of the city and help counter the forces of fatalism, disconnect and fragmentation. The project uncovered a wealth of hitherto untapped energy amongst Glasgow's citizens. People expressed a confidence, loyalty and optimism in the city that is simply not reflected in their confidence in society as a whole. The city is where people are more willing to act and it is where people feel they matter. The challenge for the leaders of Glasgow and their urban peers from Madrid to Mumbai is the same: how to unleash people's enthusiasm and belief to engage in and improve their cities.

SEPTEMBER 2020

MO	TU	WE	TH	FR	SA	SU
	1	2	3	4	5	6
7	8	9	10	11	12	13
14	15	16	17	18	19	20
21	22	23	24	25	26	27
28	29	30				

This book invites you to join us on the journey of Glasgow 2020. Over the course of the project the city of Glasgow underwent significant institutional and public policy change:

• The smoking ban was introduced across Scotland on 26 March 2006 — ahead of the rest of the UK.

• Glasgow City Council's Culture and Sport Department became an independent charitable trust in April 2007.

• Proportional representation was introduced for Scottish local authority elections on 3 May 2007 — the first part of Great Britain to have PR for town halls.

None of these changes was the result of the activities of Glasgow 2020, but they illustrate the changing nature and dynamism of the city in a relatively

OCTOBER 2020

MO	TU	WE	TH	FR	SA	SU
			1	2	3	4
5	6	7	8	9	10	11
12	13	14	15	16	17	18
19	20	21	22	23	24	25
26	27	28	29	30	31	

short timespan. The smoking ban changed the city landscape in relation to public houses, concerts and numerous social activities, especially as Glasgow has one of the highest smoking prevalence rates in Scotland at over 33 per cent of adults (a level itself significantly above the Scottish average of 27 per cent); in some of the most socially disadvantaged areas in Glasgow, smoking rates are as high as 63 per cent.[5] The introduction of proportional representation for town halls has the potential to change dramatically the political environment of the city, given the historic Labour dominance of the city council.

Glasgow is a city that has a long history of change and reinvention. The choice the city has is not between changing and not changing, but about the nature of

NOVEMBER 2020

MO	TU	WE	TH	FR	SA	SU
						1
2	3	4	5	6	7	8
9	10	11	12	13	14	15
16	17	18	19	20	21	22
23	24	25	26	27	28	29
30						

change, who owns it and who helps shape it. If Glasgow, and cities more widely, are to successfully mobilise their people, they need a new democratic story. This is not just about more committees and more transparent governance. It is about the city turning the means of producing collective goods over to its people. This project has tried to show what this means for one facet of expanding democracy in the city — of collectively imagining the future. The book shares the outcomes of this mass imagination experiment and begins to map out how the process can be expanded and deepened into the everyday governance, culture, service design and planning of cities.

When the project found a pessimistic story about the future of cities it has been about institutions running

DECEMBER 2020

MO	TU	WE	TH	FR	SA	SU
	1	2	3	4	5	6
7	8	9	10	11	12	13
14	15	16	17	18	19	20
21	22	23	24	25	26	27
28	29	30	31			

out of patience with people. When the project has found an optimistic story it has been about people, in their own small way, changing their little corner of the city for the better. It is these hopes and dreams that we must turn to and nurture.

PART 2

THE URBAN EVERY-MAN

' Glasgow is a great city. Glasgow is in trouble.
Glasgow is handsome. Glasgow is ugly.
Glasgow is kind. Glasgow is cruel.'
— William McIlvanney[6]

Glasgow's story weaves in and out of a global urban tapestry. Often abbreviated to a simple story of decline and renewal, its back-story and current circumstances provide clear points of connection with many cities across the world. Its challenges and opportunities are shared ones: climate change, inequality, radical social diversity and economic restructuring. The city has searched for ways to adapt to these changes, and carved out public interventions in the form of city boosterism and new localism. But a closer look at the city suggests neither of these approaches have yet to satisfy people's needs and aspirations for the kind of city and lives they want. A deficit of imagination about what could come next nags at Glasgow and other cities like it.

DECLINE AND REBIRTH. Glasgow emerged as a great city during the Victorian era. The city's population grew rapidly from the early 1800s onwards, fuelled by the growth of trade and commerce with the Americas and across the Empire. This Second City of Empire knew it was at the centre of power and wealth and had a corresponding self-confidence and bravado.[7] By the turn of the twentieth century, a quarter of the world's ships were built on the Clyde. As the famous saying goes, 'The Clyde made Glasgow and Glasgow made the Clyde'.

In the aftermath of the First World War, during the 1920s and 1930s, Glasgow experienced a severe and chilling depression. After a brief recovery during the Second World War the city's population peaked at 1.1 million in 1951.[8] Overcrowding resulted in a deliberate policy of relocation. People were moved from Glasgow to new towns bringing the population down to its current level — 578,790.[9] The local economy suffered a series of shocks and dislocations in the 1970s and 1980s which significantly hit remaining manufacturing in the area, and from which today's service-dominated economy emerged.[10]

These periods of social and economic change are often alluringly synthesised into a simple story of decline and renewal. One account of the city's decline manages to flatten 50 years of history into two sentences:

> ' Stalinist post-war planning decanted half the population into new towns in the green belt, and the economy naturally imploded. The Labour council then raised taxes and the middle class fled, turning the city into a vast wasteland.' [11]

Over recent years there have been numerous proclamations of the city's turnaround. Some come from public agencies based in the city, others from external sources such as the Organisation for Economic Co-operation and Development.[12] One authoritative arbiter of city fortunes world-wide, *Fodor's Travel Guide*, declared that:

> ' Modern Glasgow has undergone an urban renaissance: trendy downtown stores, a booming and diverse culture life, stylish restaurants, and air of confidence make it Scotland's most exciting city.' [13]

There is a direct relationship between the idea of
Glasgow's decline and the city's more recent renaissance,
with the latter often used to reinforce the former to
stress the scale of the transformation. The more nuanced
reality of Glasgow in recent years is deliberately lost in
the triumphalist declarations of the birth of the 'new' and
death of the 'old'.[14]

THE BOOSTER CITY. Like that of many of its peers,
the story of late twentieth-
century Glasgow is of a city and its civic leadership
trying to come to terms with population decline,
job losses and the changing nature of the economy.
But as the century came to a close it looked as if it
had found a response: *city boosterism*. This strategy
has been embraced by many city leaders as a way for
former industrial and manufacturing cities to find a
new economic base through culture, leisure, major
events and tourism. In Glasgow it has focused heavily
on positive, feel-good messages, campaigns and events.
Highlights from the last 20 years include the following.

Mr Happy:
The use of slogans to define Glasgow began in the
1980s with the 'Glasgow's Miles Better' advertising
campaign. The campaign was accompanied by the
Mr Happy character from Roger Hargreaves' 1970s
cartoon creations, the *Mr Men*. The character's smiling
expression and bright yellow colour was seen as a
positive, fun image, which people of all ages could
identify with. In 1987 David Steel, David Owen,
Margaret Thatcher and Neil Kinnock agreed to appear
alongside Mr Happy in a series of adverts promoting

Glasgow. This campaign is widely credited with changing the way that Glasgow was perceived within Scotland and across the UK, and helped Glasgow secure the 1988 Garden Festival and the 1990 Capital of Culture.

Capital of culture:
Glasgow became the sixth European city to be awarded Capital of Culture status by the European Union, which put it alongside the previous cultural heavyweight hosts — Amsterdam, Athens, Berlin, Florence and Paris. The city staged over 3400 public events, by artists from 23 countries, 40 major works were commissioned in the performing and visual arts, and 60 world premieres in theatre and dance took place. Glasgow's Capital of Culture became a reference point for other cities looking to use culture and the arts to promote themselves and boost their international profile.

The Armadillo:
Boosterism requires iconic symbols. Glasgow has a high concentration of residential high-rises — more than any other city in the UK. But the building increasingly used to promote Glasgow is the Clyde Auditorium. Designed by Sir Norman Foster and completed in 1997, it sits alongside the banks of the Clyde and hosts conferences, concerts and exhibitions. For visibly obvious reasons it is known locally as the Armadillo.

Festivals:
Since the late 1980s Glasgow has been spawning festivals at a rate of knots. The demise of Mayfest, Glasgow's annual arts and cultural festival in 1997,

was a blow to the city's pride, but it did not put the brakes on the flowering of festivals everywhere. Some were citywide, some based in specific areas of the city. Glasgow International Jazz Festival, was followed by The Celtic Connections Festival; Glasgay!, the annual lesbian, gay, bisexual and transgender arts festival; the West End Festival; the Merchant City Festival; and more recently the Comedy Festival and the International Film Festival. All of these received public sponsorship and support from public agencies in the city.

Executed with considerable gusto, the boosterism strategy has led to gains for Glasgow. The Miles Better campaign was originally devised to change the perceptions of external audiences, particularly middle-class media, business decision-makers and opinion formers in London. It is widely regarded as having succeeded in this. For example, *The Economist* wrote in 2004 that the campaign, along with 'I Love New York', is 'one of the few successful city rebranding advertising campaigns. Tourists came flooding in, halting years of economic decline.' [15] Tourism now accounts for 7.6 per cent of all jobs in Glasgow,[16] serving 2.8 million tourists.[17] Michael Kelly, former Lord Provost and one of the architects of the campaign, talks about the welcome but unintended side-effect of the campaign's popularity with people and businesses inside Glasgow, helping prompt more positive self-perceptions of the city.[18] These perceptions were given sustenance by new jobs and services coming to Glasgow and a much needed clean-up programme of many of its public buildings.

Fifteen years on Glasgow is still pursuing the same strategy, seemingly with some continued success.

For example, in 2006 the city was nominated by
Frommer's Travel Guide as one of their top ten world
destinations[19] (the only European destination on the list)
and readers of *Conde Nast Traveller* voted Glasgow their
favourite UK city.[20] With a sense that major events and
civic promotion is working for Glasgow, the city now has
its eye set on hosting the 2014 Commonwealth Games.[21]

THE LIMITS OF THE
CULTURAL ARMS RACE.

The relentless positive
rhetoric of the booster
city is partly responsible for the uncomplicated
story of Glasgow's decline and rebirth. The constant
proclamations of success are justified on the basis that
they benefit the city. Confidence will breed confidence,
tourists will visit, businesses will relocate and students
will enrol. But despite the gains this approach has
brought for Glasgow and cities like it, there are signs
that the wind is starting to come out of the sails. What
felt radical when Dublin, Barcelona and Glasgow
embarked on the city boosterism path in the late 1980s
and early 1990s, now feels derivative and is delivering
diminishing returns. When every city has commissioned
a celebrity architect and pedestrianised a cultural quarter,
distinctiveness gets reduced to a formula.

Some of these doubts have surfaced in Glasgow.
The city's latest marketing slogan 'Glasgow: Scotland
with style' has met with less than universal approval
within Glasgow, failing to tap into the Glaswegian sense
of humour and irreverence the way Mr Happy did.
There are concerns that the overemphasis on Glasgow
as the Second City of Shopping has left its cultural

offering thin. One serious charge turns on what all this culture and creativity is for? Some of the booster city's harsher critiques accuse it of co-opting culture in the name of increasing property values and high-end consumers. For example, during the late 1980s and early 1990s a group of artists and writers formed a group called the Workers' City[22] and campaigned against the amount of money spent on what it saw as a sanitized, publicly sanitised art.[23]

Glasgow is not alone in finding the city boosterism formula wanting. In 2004 Barcelona fell out of love with its culture and big-event-led strategy. Although the strategy had worked well to mobilise and transform the city around the 1992 Olympics, by 2004 the Forum de Culture it had lost its power to engage and the event was widely regarded as a failure and prompted much soul-searching in the city about its future direction.[24]

There are clearly limits to what a cultural arms race can achieve. Many cities that have claimed to turn the corner, such as Manchester and Dundee, are still losing population, while Glasgow's long population decline has only slightly tipped upwards.[25]

THE POTENTIAL OF LOCALISM.

Thus boosterism can take cities only so far. However, over the last few years another response has begun to assemble and surface. Politicians have been falling over themselves to show how keen they are to give away power to communities and local institutions. There has been David Miliband's talk of 'double devolution', Ruth Kelly's interest in 'devolution to the doorsteps', and similar mood music from David Cameron.

These signals amount to a second wave response to thinking about the challenges facing post-industrial cities. However, while they do reflect something of a shift in thinking at the centre, it is unclear whether the right words are being matched by the right actions. There are at least three fault lines scoring the potential pathway of city-led localism.

First, excessive centralisation over the past 30 years will take some undoing. Under the governments of Margaret Thatcher and Tony Blair there has been a fundamental shift to a command and control centre where power is concentrated in the hands of the prime minister and Treasury.[26] Across successive areas, local government has been reduced to being administrators of central policy. In financial terms, lacking control of business rates, councils raise less and less of the money they spend. If councils want to take different decisions from those made nationally, which involve higher spending, they have to increase council taxes.

The term 'double devolution' itself shows the inherent problems in this debate and the fuzzy thinking of the centre. 'Devolution', in Enoch Powell's famous definition, asserts 'power devolved is power retained'. Fundamentally, the UK's recent experience of devolution has not involved the centre rethinking itself or its relationship with other bodies in terms of consistently shifting power downwards and outwards.[27]

Second, there has been little progress in mapping out how the localism agenda fits with the realities, needs and aspirations of our towns and cities.

While cities — rather than firms or nations — are recognised as the primary units driving economic

innovation and productivity, finding the appropriate
political and institutional arrangements to match
has largely stalled, as illustrated by the disappointed
responses from city leaders to the 2006 UK government
local government white paper. There is a danger that
the debate about city regions is failing to progress and is
instead creating numerous institutional and partnership
bodies which obfuscate, confuse and entrench the
sense that power really still lies in the centre.
Glasgow, like many other cities in the UK, eyes cities
in places like Germany and the US where there is
a far greater degree of financial and political autonomy
at the level of the city.

Third, a new idea of 'the local' is needed
which includes but goes beyond city hall. Many of
the structures of new localism, such as community
participation and power sharing seem remarkably
similar to the old local-authority-centred ones. This may
explain why the chance to sit on public service and
neighbourhood boards or any of the myriad of new
partnership structures remains less than appealing to
most people. At the moment there is a danger that most
people's response to the queue of politicians proffering
their varied salvers of power will be a polite, 'thanks,
but no thanks'. Paul Slatter, Director of the Birmingham
Community Empowerment Network, explains the root
of the problem in terms of the difference between
communities being *given* power and communities
taking power.[28]

THE END OF THE LINE. Despite the dominant story of decline and rebirth, Glasgow's wider experience reveals a series of issues untouched, which neither boosterism nor localism seem able to adequately engage with. These gaps, omissions and problems that Glasgow is experiencing point to the limitations of much of the mainstream urban response of the last 20 years. Many of these problems are shared by cities elsewhere.

Growing economic, social and spatial inequality:
European cities across the board are experiencing growing inequalities and entrenched social exclusion. This is not unusual; the profitability of many city spaces in North America and Western Europe has been coupled with sharpening socio-economic inequalities and what Gordon McLeod has called 'the institutional displacement and social exclusion of certain marginalized groups'.[29]

Glasgow is a city of extremes and contrasts, of huge wealth concentrations as well as extreme relative poverty. In 2006 the city contained 1,076 millionaires — the fifth highest total in the UK; Edinburgh had 1,301 millionaires — the second highest.[30] Greater Glasgow has nine of the top 20 property streets in Scotland.[31] In 2005 according to Scottish Business Monitor 113 of Scotland's top 500 companies (23%) were located in Glasgow.[32]

Glasgow's housing tenure has changed dramatically with owner occupation rising from 24 per cent in 1981 to 49 per cent in 2001. This transformation has been uneven across the city and region, with rates of owner occupation varying in the Greater Glasgow area from 88 per cent in Eastwood to 34 per cent in Maryhill, Woodside and North Glasgow.[33] The city contains 226 of the neighbourhoods judged to be among the 5 per cent most deprived in Scotland; 70 per cent of the national total, one-third of Glasgow's entire population live in these areas.[34] It contains the largest number of further and higher education students in Scotland totalling 118,000 enrolled students in 2003/04. At the same time the number of school leavers going into further education was 21 per cent compared with a Scottish average of 31 per cent.[35]

These escalating inequalities find form in the physical spaces and places of Glasgow. One such place is Crown Street in the Gorbals. Here commentators have argued that although this award-winning regeneration scheme was developed with civic purposes in mind it has ended up reinforcing social polarisation.

> ' Elite designers have taken Crown Street's working class landscape, idealized it and estranged it from its roots. Likewise, they have empowered the young, the middle class and the outsider at the expense of the vulnerable, the working class and the local.'[36]

Deepening divisions and fragmentation within the labour market:

In addition to the socio-spatial fragmentation that has emerged in Glasgow and other cities, new divides are appearing in the labour market as the skills gap widens. With more and more emphasis on knowledge-intensive sectors, a kind of 'labour apartheid' develops, with workers in knowledge and creative industries pulling away but increasingly dependent on an army of service workers to facilitate their lifestyles. Pacific Quay, the location of the new media centre in Glasgow, provides a telling example. As some have pointed out, a media and science centre was never going to provide work for the 'de-skilled, benefit-dependent, ageing population of Govan'.[37] Instead, as the self-titled 'Friend of Zanetti' continued, there is 'a widening income and opportunity gap between professional and managerial workers and those at the lower end who lack the skills for the new economy'.[38] In post-regeneration Govan, the population has fallen by more than 20 per cent in the last decade and 51 per cent of adults are unemployed, all this in the shadow of gleaming new industrial units and offices.[39]

Breakdown of trust among people:

The most recent social values survey found that just 26 per cent of us believe that most other people can be trusted, compared with over two-thirds who thought this in the 1950s.[40] Symbolic and symptomatic of this decline in trust is the rise of a panoply of human, physical and technical methods to monitor and regulate behaviour in cities, including systems of surveillance such as CCTV, private security and architectural design. Punitive institutional responses to perceived transgressions and misdemeanours seem to have had a limited effect in Glasgow, which has an unenviable record in relation to violent crime as 'the murder capital of Europe'. The level of violent crime continues to yo-yo up and down and official figures are expected to rise for 2006/07.[41]

Gap between people and public institutions:

Cities have adapted well to an economy based less around mass-reproduced products and more around the creation of customised end experiences. From call centres to gyms, tanning salons to PC repair shops, new season ticket deals to personalised concerts, and life coaches to falafels, cities are thriving on the spending power and life-style demands of individuals searching for individual, personalised experiences.[42] But for all their dynamism and ability to connect with people's material aspirations, our cities are struggling to configure themselves to help resolve more everyday social and environmental needs. Public bodies, quangos and services struggle to find ways to communicate with and inspire changes in public behaviour while people remain untrusting, or simply cannot see the results of the activity undertaken on their collective behalf.

At the same time political engagement is in crisis in Scotland and the UK. The last two UK general elections saw the lowest turnout in post-war times — 59.4 per cent in 2001 and 61.2 per cent in 2005.[43] Fault lines are opening up along the lines of place and class: in the 2005 UK election the turnout level was 70 per cent among the AB group and 54 per cent among the DE group, the largest gap ever recorded at a UK election.[44]

Masculine alienation caused by shifting status of men in the city:

Deindustrialisation and the decline of manufacturing work have eroded traditional gender roles. Working-class men, previously 'breadwinners' and with a strong sense of collective identity, have either joined the ranks of the

unemployed or found work in the service sector
with a significant effect on self-identity formation.
The Glasgow economy now has some of the highest
levels of economic exclusion in all of the UK. The overall
economic activity rate of the city hides huge disparities
and the fact that these are simultaneously 'good times'
and 'bad times' for parts of the population. In Greater
Glasgow Bridgeton East has the highest percentage
of the working-age population economically inactive:
66 per cent, while the lowest is Cumbernauld at 19.4 per
cent.[45] In public health, the now legendary 'Shettleston
Man' lives to an average age of 64 years. What has
been less commented on is the gender dimension here:
'Shettleston Woman' living in the same environment lives
to an average of 75 years, a life expectancy gender gap
of 11 years, which is nearly twice the Scottish average.[46]

THE IMAGINATION DEFICIT. With the emergence
or in some cases
reinforcement of this set of messy problems, the Glasgow
experience hints at widening gaps between the needs
of cities, their people and the kinds of local action
governments at different levels are configured for.
The problem is deeper than city hall lacking the right
technical fix; instead there is a more profound loss in the
vitality of urban imagination about the kind of shared
futures we want in our cities. Richard Sennett sets out
the problem:

> ' Something has gone wrong, radically wrong,
>   in our conception of what a city itself should be.
>   We need to imagine just what a clean, safe, efficient,

dynamic, stimulating, just city would look like concretely
— we need those images to confront critically our masters
with what they should be doing — and just this critical
imagination of the city is weak.' [47]

Sennett points the finger at modernism for creating
'closed' urban landscapes through an 'over-determination'
of our cities' visual forms and social functions. He
describes Le Corbusier's 1922 Plan Voison for Paris
as 'a portent of the freezing of the urban imagination'.[48]
Its masterplan conceived of replacing most of the centre
of Paris with uniform buildings and eliminating most
human-scale street-level activity. Sennett argues that
since then zoning, regulation and rules have proliferated
in urban development and planning and with it brought a
brittleness in the urban fabric, as evidenced in the rapid
decay of modern buildings. The average lifespan of new
public housing in Britain is 40 years, while it is a mere 35
years for office buildings in New York.[49]
　　　Glasgow displays characteristics of the modernist
closed city with its attraction to 'big' one-off solutions to
problems. There is a lineage running through Glasgow's
idea of progress that sees the appeal of the epic and
monumental — from mass council building in the 1950s
to motorway developments in the 1960s and shopping
developments in the early twenty-first century. From this
perspective, the UK-wide competition to be awarded a
supercasino — which Glasgow bid for and lost in January
2007 — is emblematic of its predilection for big projects
and of the imagination deficit in the closed city.[50]
　　　Evidence of the closed city can also be seen

in reactive responses to public behaviour where the emphasis is squarely on cracking down on anti-social behaviour rather than looking at what might constitute social behaviour and interaction and how it might be best encouraged. This is far from a uniquely British phenomenon. In 2006 Barcelona passed its *l'ordenança de convivència* (order of cohabitation) setting out a long list of urban crimes, from writing graffiti to making inappropriate uses of public spaces, which people can be fined for.

The limitations of the dominant urban strategies of city boosterism and localism examined earlier in this chapter can themselves be understood as the corollary of the narrow mental and physical landscape of the closed city. Tweaking the rules under the banner of double devolution as to who gets to decide the detail of whatever policy directive does little to change the situation; the game is still being played with the same restricted rules of an essentially closed system.

If cities are to break free from the closed city, they will need to begin to imagine a different future and engage the most abundant and potent source of new ideas and practices a city has — its people. In order to do this, cities have to be open to asking some big questions. What kind of cities do we want to live in? Who has the energy and impetus to make change in them happen? How will people be involved in the process of change? What kind of support do they need to help shape their shared futures? These are all political questions.

If the challenge for the future of cities is political

then the answer needs to come in democratic form.
But as logical as that may seem, cities are not currently
configured for democratic conversation about the future.
One of the key obstacles to this has been the emergence
of a pervasive 'official future'. It is to this that we will
turn next.

PART 3

THE OFFICIAL FUTURE

The pictures in this section are illustrated
wishes made by 6 year old's (who will be 21 in 2020).

' On the day when eutropia's inhabitants feel the grip of
weariness and no one can bear any longer his job, his
relatives, his house and his life, debts, the people he must
greet or who greet him, then the whole citizenry decides
to move to the next city, which is there waiting for them,
empty and good as new; there each will take up a new job,
a different wife, will see another landscape on opening his
window, and will spend his time with different pastimes,
friends, gossip.'
— Italo Calvino, *Invisible Cities*[51]

This chapter explores how Glasgow is constrained by
the emergence of a dominant institutional official future.
The power dynamics and the impact of the official future
are mapped out including, perhaps most importantly,
how the official future can swallow people's sense
of agency.

Official futures can be found lurking in the
subconscious hum of most companies, organisations
and governments, a set of implicit assumptions that set
the parameters for strategy and decision-making.
Their danger lies in their conventional wisdom turning
into collective self-delusion. Global Business Network,
which originally coined the term, has a collection of
parables cataloguing the woes of blue chip corporations
who slipped into the comfort zone of their official future
and never asked what would happen if they were wrong
— very wrong. One example is the communications
firm AT&T. In the 1980s AT&T failed to consider that
there was even an outside chance that internet services
would attain popular appeal and so declined the US
government's offer of a free transfer (and monopoly) of
the administration of the internet.[52]

In cities, the official future is a reflection of who holds power and has become a way of consolidating it. At its heart it is a series of received wisdoms and understandings, embedded in language that is hard to understand and which characterises the conversations of institutional agencies in the city. The official future conditions and constrains the choices the city believes it has and seeps into everyday governance and decision-making.

In Glasgow we find the official future told by a spidery organogram of institutions in a web of strategy documents, development plans, mission statements and conference speeches, and woven through every subject area from health to Glasgow's bid to host the 2014 Commonwealth Games.[53] While not completely unified or uniform, Glasgow's institutional voices are imbued with a common tone, language and content, and all point in the same direction.

Glasgow's official future can be understood in three dimensions: *content, style and authorship.* In other words, *what* gets said, *how* it gets said and *who* gets to say it.

AUTHORSHIP. People being authors of change in their cities is a powerful idea, but in Glasgow what gets talked about and conceived is dominated by institutional voices. This institutional authority is not new. For decades Glasgow was shaped by the strong ideas and self-confidence shown by the Corporation, the elected city council. This had a huge reach over the lives of its citizens and a belief in looking after them from cradle to grave. This was a two-way contract: the City Fathers saw themselves as responsible for every aspect of the city, and the people looked to them to provide housing, hospitals, schools, electricity, gas and water. A section in *Glasgow Our City*, a council-produced book from 1957, aimed at school children, makes clear the omnipotent power of the Corporation:

' You wake up in the morning in a house built by the Corporation and wash your hands and face in water brought by the Corporation all the way from Loch Katrine. You go to school on a Corporation bus, and the building and the

books are all Corporation property. A Corporation teacher
looks after your mind and a Corporation doctor looks after
your body. After school, you can play in a Corporation park,
swim in a Corporation pond or skate in a Corporation hall.
The evening you can spend reading a book borrowed from a
Corporation library.' [54]

Half a century on the institutional power map is much
messier. The Glasgow Corporation was abolished in
local government reorganisation in 1974 and replaced by
Glasgow District Council, which was then superseded by
Glasgow City Council in 1996. The map is complex with
numerous organisations and overlapping responsibilities.
The city council does not have responsibility for public
health, hospitals or social housing — despite popular
public perceptions that think otherwise. The Scottish
and UK parliaments hold significant sway, and a
revealing example of the number of agencies at work
was contained in a recent document that listed 23 'main'
economic policy documents for the city. [55]

Public agencies, including Greater Glasgow and
Clyde NHS Board, Glasgow Housing Association (which
has responsibility for the city's stock of former council
housing) and Scottish Enterprise Glasgow, all have the
power to shape long-term policies, allocate significant
resources and somedeliver services. The private sector
has a number of bodies that attempt to develop a
coherent local voice, most notably Glasgow Chamber of
Commerce and the Federation of Small Businesses.

However, for all the institutional messy diffuseness,
the authorship over Glasgow's future does not seem
to have decisively opened up since the days of the
Corporation. The biggest step forward in systematically

sharing authorship more widely is through the city's well-established Community Planning Partnership, which brings together Glasgow's key public, private, community and voluntary representatives. It has set out its vision in its community plan, *Our Vision 2005–10.*[56] However, even this has its stated primary aim of 'delivering better, more joined-up public services in the city'.[57] As with other public consultation activities undertaken in the city there is a sense of fatigue among people and a feeling that many of the real decisions about agenda, direction and resources have already been taken elsewhere.

CONTENT. The core content of Glasgow's official future has five basic themes: step change and transformation; a world-class city; opportunity and choice; a narrow optimism; one voice and one vision.

Step change and transformation:

' Step change reflects the improvement necessary to move Glasgow from its current trajectory to one which will realise the vision. Glasgow has made a step change from "problem city" to "city of opportunities". In ten years, Glasgow should be defined by strength and leadership, rather than the processes of regeneration, however successful.' [58]

The idea of 'step change' is one of the central mantras of the official future. Thus, statements have a completely circular nature, beginning, 'We must be more creative — more of the same is not good enough to achieve step change' and then concluding, 'Success for Glasgow will mean achieving step change'.[59] Behind this is a set of contradictory messages. On the one hand it praises the change and progress made so far, on the other, it says that a transformation is needed for the future.

It thus implicitly argues that more of the same is not good enough for the future and then poses a future that is a hyped-up, accelerated version of what has already happened.

Step change and transformation are also problematic as core propositions for deep psychological reasons, as Charles Roxburgh explains.[60] First, is the concept of *anchoring* — as humans we naturally remain anchored to our past. This is reinforced by *aversion loss,* whereby people tend to be more concerned about the risk of loss than excited about the prospect of gain. Finally, *the endowment effect* creates a strong desire to hang on to what we own; simply owning something — anything — makes it seem more valuable. In combination, these factors mean that people usually do not want to believe in any story that involves a significant amount of change for them.

A world-class city:

> ' I knock Glasgow's competitors at every opportunity I get.
> Not Edinburgh or other Scottish cities, but Barcelona,
> Amsterdam, Prague, and the other short-stay destinations.'
> — Glasgow City marketing executive

Official Glasgow celebrates its new-found status
as a shopping mecca and top tourist destination,
revelling in the city's new role as a place for conspicuous
consumption, affluent lifestyles and global city breaks.
There are several problems with this. One is that
it can be seen as promoting a way of living that is
unsustainable — both environmentally and in terms of
people's disposable income, growing levels of debt and
life satisfaction.

Another problem is the clutter of cities on the
world-class trail with a familiar formula supporting
their campaign — shopping, tourism, mega-events,
cultural events, iconic architecture and casinos
— leaving little room for distinctiveness. But the bigger
problem is perhaps the shallow set of attributes that cities
tend to test their world-class mettle against. What about
a world-class city judged on its civility, the playability
of its public space, or being a good place to grow
old? It is striking, for example, that as yet no other city
has seriously sought to match the 'world-class' green
credentials of Dongtan — the new-build eco-city on
Chongming Island near Shanghai.[61]

Opportunity and choice:

> ' The problem with Glasgow is the attitudes of some of its
> people. They don't want to work, they want something for
> nothing. They are happy living on benefits and the only
> aspirations they have is for their benefits to go up.'
> — Glasgow journalist

The official future talks the language of 'opportunity',
'choice' and 'diversity', but does not really believe in or
practise them. It poses a set menu, rather than à la carte,
confident that it knows best. For all the rhetoric of
new ways of working, partnership and collaboration,
there can still be a very old-fashioned top-down
approach in parts of institutional Glasgow that retains
a faith that experts and professionals must hold all the
answers. This 'we know best' approach can very quickly
boil over into a sense of frustration, spurred by a sense
that institutional Glasgow has done its part by presenting
the right choices and is left perplexed at why people are
failing to choose the right option. There is an implicit

belief that people are poor because of low aspirations and Glaswegians are unhealthy because they won't accept responsibility, make the right choice and eat healthily.

A narrow optimism:

> ' Glasgow doesn't matter. Scotland can live with a Glasgow where ultimately power and the economic powerhouses lie elsewhere in Edinburgh and the East. '
> — Public affairs adviser

These are relatively good times for Glasgow's economy — with a 66 per cent employment rate among the economically active — a 25-year high — and 60,000 new jobs created in the last decade.[62] However, behind these figures there is a sense of nervousness and anxiety. Twenty-eight per cent of the working-age population are economically inactive.[63] For all the claims about the bright new future only 11,000 new jobs are predicted as likely to be created in the next decade — one-sixth the previous total.[64]

Below this there is a somewhat unreflective set of assumptions about economic growth and how Glasgow can move up the international league table of cities and 'grow its global market share'.[65] The documents of the official future now do pay reference to such issues as 'sustainability', 'carbon footprints' and the importance of balancing 'wealth and well-being'. But the thrust and drive is unremittingly about economic growth, competition and globalisation. In some accounts, everything — art, culture, creativity, leisure — seems to be reduced to playing a supporting role for the economy.

One voice, one vision:

> ' Glasgow and Edinburgh need to become one mega-city
> working together. Who cares if the people are against it?
> We should just do it.'
> — Public official in Glasgow

In the words of the Queen song of the 1980s, the official future is about 'one voice, one vision'. This is not that different from the Glasgow of the 1940s and 1950s when the city faced the future with a modernist certainty that planning was the answer. The Glasgow of the early twenty-first century is still informed by the modernist dream, this time with free-market private development and economic growth seen as the savours of the city.

The contemporary official future has perhaps an even more potent sense of homogeneity than previous eras. It implicitly seems to say, if you don't agree with this, your views don't really matter and says so with an impatience of a parent speaking to a child, and little space for pluralism, dissent, discussion and negotiation.

Official Glasgow believes it has to spruce up the local population for global challenges and realities, but also recognises that across many fronts people are not locally doing or choosing what they are meant to do according to the official account.

STYLE AND LANGUAGE.

' The Glasgow "Scotland with Style" brand is a holistic communications tool. From education to tourism, retail to transport, events to investment, the brand will continue to deliver a consistent and coherent message driving forward a range of different partner activities on the national and international stage.'
— Glasgow's City Marketing Bureau [66]

' A greater degree of economic specialisation is desirable. Specialisation, with its accompanying productivity benefits, is a vital source of competitive advantage for cities. Although it is possible to be over-specialised, Glasgow does not fit this description, at least not in terms of its sectoral composition. If anything, Glasgow may be over-specialised in lower-productivity occupations, lower down the "value chain".'
— Glasgow Economic Forum [67]

Like many groups and cliques, the authors of the official future have evolved a style and language of their own, which can become an obstacle to public comprehension of the vision of the future expressed by public institutions. It is a specialist, jargon and acronym-heavy language, which regulates — sometimes intentionally, sometimes unintentionally — who has a voice and who has power. It reflects the need for institutions to create a short-hand for shared understandings and assumptions, part of the process of 'getting things done' — but the collateral damage in this often ends up being wider understanding of their version of the future.

For example, Glasgow City Marketing Bureau's 'Scotland with Style' branding strategy aims to attract people to Glasgow — an important part of the city's future. A press release explains that these people are part of a 'style pyramid', which is made up of 'exclusive style setters', 'early style adopters', 'then capital leaders' on level three, and at the bottom, 'style followers'.[68] To a marketing outsider, it is hard to see who exactly these different groups of people are, why they are coming to Glasgow and what they will bring to the city.

Advocates of the official future cite that we live in times of unprecedented change, challenge and complexity, but that does not explain fully why their language mystifies and they use such complex terminology.

Sixty years ago, the generation coming out of the Second World War faced challenges and pressures that were seemingly insurmountable. The two Beveridge reports on full employment and the welfare state were written in an accessible form, became best-sellers, and the language used — slaying 'the Five Giants' — became part of the public conversation. If we managed to rise to that challenge then, why can we not do so now?

The language of the official future inhabits a separate world, which is not the same world as that of the people of the city.

THE COSTS OF
THE OFFICIAL FUTURE.
While Glasgow's official future might be insulated from the everyday lives and aspirations of the city its people, its costs are not. Three sets of negative impacts can be identified: disengagement and disempowerment, disbelief and distrust, opposition and confusion.

Disengagement and disempowerment:
People felt that some of the implicit messages they picked up from the official future could be interpreted as 'Don't worry about the future, it has already been sorted out'.

Glasgow already has high levels of disengagement, with some of the lowest electoral turnouts in the UK. For example, Shettleston — which has the lowest life expectancy in the UK[69] — had the third lowest political turnout at the 2001 General Election with 39.7 percent of individuals registered casting a vote.[70] Quantitative research conducted for the council also illuminates the level of democratic disconnect with only a quarter of respondents agreeing that they felt they could influence decisions made in their area, and only a third believe their comments would be listened to by decision-makers. There appears to be a lack of faith in traditional processes of consultation and engagement, with no more than a third rating as effective any method of influencing decisions from contacting a councillor or MSP to joining a group.[71]

Disbelief and distrust:

Walter Fisher explains that what people do when they encounter a story is test its coherence and fidelity — does the story hold together and does it match our own beliefs and experiences?[72] The many public events and conversations Demos had with people, both inside and outside institutions, suggested that the official future scored low on coherence and fidelity. People feel that the values and beliefs of the main official institutions of the city are not the same as the values that they hold themselves. Often people could not quite put their finger on what they felt was wrong, but could not fully trust what was motivating the institution in question and suspected covert motivations such as commercial gain or guarding wealth and status. Such suspicion clearly has implications for people's levels of trust in institutional decision-making.

Sometimes we encountered people who believed in parts of the official future. Clearly Glasgow has to develop economically. Culture is one of the city's great successes historically and in recent years. Shopping and tourism bring big bucks to the city's tills. However, even inside institutions, which publicly were signed up to the official future, there was little real support and no genuine enthusiasm for the wholesale worldview carried with it.

Opposition and confusion:

Where the official future is not widely believed, then the message and messenger can quickly start to be attacked through the emergence of counter-stories that call into question the official version. In Glasgow the mismatch

between the official future and people's perceptions
is heightened by stories in the local media where a
series of symbolic stories and images reoccur. Poverty is
represented by boarded-up houses, crime by burnt-out
cars, youth by track-suited gangs, and drugs by syringes
lying on waste ground.

We found this split view of Glasgow left people
in a state of debilitating confusion, on the one hand
people hearing the hype about the city and on the other
its social collapse. As one woman said in a story-telling
workshop, 'What's going on? Are we a great city or not?'
The 'one voice one vision' insistence of the official future
effectively leaves no room for exploring or testing the
different versions on offer. Fundamentally, 'the official
future' faces two ways at the same time. It presents
itself to the public as all-powerful and all-knowing
— acknowledging only one true voice. Yet at the same
time the official future has to admit that all it wants,
desires and cherishes is actually beyond its reach,
and is contingent and shaped by many external factors
— economic, political, social and environmental flows,
shifts and jolts.

The malaise of the official future is not unique
to Glasgow. It was also in evidence in the events run
in Gothenburg, Helsinki and Stockholm. For example,
in a Helsinki workshop participants felt that there was
a dominant discourse of change that mismatched the
reality of stasis. In Stockholm, workshop participants
were frustrated with the official image marketed to the
world and felt that it missed what they valued in their
city. In Gothenburg, many were concerned with the
city's heavy focus on an icon-led refit of the harbour-

side. And across all of the cities a similar language, tone, basic presumptions and values to Glasgow's could be discerned, with each city trying to get ahead of its nearest competitors and benchmark itself a few notches higher up the city league table than its contemporaries.

The dichotomy of power/powerlessness underlies the contradictions and fragility at the heart of 'the official future' and points to the wider fragility of the current resurgence of cities. There is then an urgent need to find some new shared stories to help bridge the gaps between cities, their people and the future. To do so requires a better understanding of the everyday story-making capacity of people and cities.

PART 4

THE POWER OF STORY

' What, Glasgow? — The city, not the film. — The city is
the film. — Oh come on. — I tell you. Right then, look.
Renfield Street, marchers, banners, slogans. Read the
message, hear the chant. — Lights! Cameras!'
— Edwin Morgan, A City[73]

The stories we tell matter because they indicate how
much agency we believe we have to shape the world
around us. This chapter explores the rising stock of
stories and the opportunities for better tapping into the
innate storytelling abilities of people and cities to help
generate new shared stories about our collective futures.

THE STORY IMPERATIVE. As much science as art,
story-telling is biologically
hard-wired into us through our genes. This story
imperative first shows when we are about four years
old as we begin to be able to put nouns and verbs
together and describe the world around us. This is also
the point from which we carry our earliest memories
into adulthood. As such, scientists have placed the idea
of story next to language in understanding what makes
us human. It is how we learn, remember and organise
our understanding of time — the past, the present and
the future.[74] Integral then to human development, stories
have always been with us, from Greek myths and pagan
legends to Hollywood thrillers and kitchen-sink dramas.
A story has a sense of flow and a beginning, a middle
and an ending — the last of which is as defining as when
the final credits roll in a film. Robert McKee has stated
that a story has certain key elements: a plot, characters,
a journey and a resolution or attempted resolution.[75]
The power and reach of story plays with and touches

our emotions, senses and intuition and can throw up all sorts of questions about how we interpret right and wrong, and the morals we have. The stories we tell have a relationship with place and space — a point relevant to Glasgow 2020 — and have an added salience in an age of widespread cynicism and doubt.

Christopher Booker, in his magisterial treatise *The Seven Basic Plots*,[76] identifies the principal plots by which most stories, created by diverse cultures, are structured:

- **Overcoming the monster**
  stories of the supernatural, horror stories.
- **Rags to riches**
  stories of personal transformation.
- **The Quest**
  where answering 'a call' leads to a life-renewing goal.
- **Voyage and return**
  the travel and surprise of another world.
- **Comedy**
  the only genre with a tendency to reconciliation and unity.
- **Tragedy**
  where the hero faces by the end love and/or death.
- **Rebirth**
  seen in fairytales of princes and princesses.

Across these seven archetypes, Booker identifies a 'universal plot' characterised by shadow, light and by that part of human nature that can be symbolised as 'dark power'. If this leads to a complete resolution 'the ending shows us how dark power can be overthrown, with the light ending triumphant'.[77]

THE NEW
STORY PARADIGM.

At times, storytelling has been deeply mistrusted — most of the second half of Plato's *The Republic* is an emphatic exposition of why storytellers should be banished for the health of society, according to Denning.[78] But recently storytelling has been embraced and championed as the must-have tool in a wide range of fields, from savvy businesses to efficient medical practices. The rising stock of stories can be seen as a part of the shift away from the focus on logical, linear, computer-like capabilities and the metaphor of the machine as an agent of change. Instead there has been a growing interest in issues of meaning, values, ambiguity, fluidity and non-linear notions of thinking which give centre stage to subjectivity and context.

Daniel Pink has dubbed this phenomenon 'the rise of the conceptual age', and accounts for the rising cache of storytelling partly as a consequence of the internet and the limits of information age:

> ' Today facts are ubiquitous, nearly free, and available at the speed of light… When facts become so widely available and instantly accessible, each one becomes less valuable.
> What begins to matter more is the ability to place these facts in context and to deliver them with emotional impact.'[79]

Annette Simons puts it even more strongly:

> ' People don't want information. They are up to their eyeballs in information. They want faith — faith in you, your goals, your success, in the story you tell. It is faith that moves

mountains not facts. Facts do not give birth to faith. Faith needs a story to sustain it.'[80]

The rise of story and storytelling can be seen in this context, of trying to find pathways of simply and honestly explaining an increasingly complex, messy world. Fisher argues that this shift amounts to the emergence of a new story paradigm.[81] He explains the difference between this and more traditional rationality-based forms of communication and organisation.

Principle of the traditional rational paradigm
* People are essentially rational.
* We make decisions on the basis of arguments.
* Rationality is determined by how much we know and how well we argue.
  The world is a set of logical puzzles that we can
* solve through rational analysis.

Principle of the new story paradigm
* People are essentially storytellers.
* We make decisions on the basis of good reasons.
* History, biography, culture and character determine what we consider good reasons.
* Story rationality is determined by a variety of factors about story: who creates them, how they are told, context, coherence and fidelity.
* The world is a set of stories from which we choose, and thus constantly re-create, our lives.

The practical value of story is making itself felt in a wide variety of specific, and sometimes unexpected, contexts.

Leadership:

Stephen Denning, a writer and former programme director of knowledge management at the World Bank has earned himself the status of storytelling guru.[82] In the mid 1990s he instigated an organisational revolution at the World Bank with a 97-word story about a health worker in Zambia who was struggling to get good information about effective treatment of malaria. In an organisation that had a well-earned reputation for resisting change, this simple story helped staff and managers envision a different kind of future for their organisation — from one where its raison d'être was to lend money to developing countries to one whose purpose was knowledge sharing; from money bank to knowledge bank.

Information management:

One of the most well-known tales about the transformative power of storytelling in organisations is told by John Seely Brown a former senior executive of Xerox.[83] He was tasked with finding a better way to train the company's 25,000 repair personnel spread across the world; sending them all back to a centralised training camp once a year was proving costly and ineffective. Instead of constructing the mother of all technical trouble shooting manuals, Seely Brown hired an anthropologist and sent him to spend six months hanging out with the repair guys in the field. This research revealed that the repair personnel resolved copier problems by constructing scenarios and stories of what might have gone wrong with the machine and that there was a strong culture of sharing these stories in cafés over lunch with colleagues.

Armed with this understanding of how knowledge develops and moves around, Seely Brown developed a personal story bank called Eureka. This system has made a 10 per cent saving in repair time and parts, and has been valued at worth over $100 million to the company. It has also made company heroes of the most prolific copier storytellers whose tales and profiles have travelled around the globe.

Public service outcomes:

The power of story is increasingly used in a variety of settings not just by big business. The developing concept of 'narrative health care' is seen by a growing constituency as further using the social model of health, and providing an alternative to the medical model of health where the professionals traditionally have the knowledge and the patient has little say.[84] Narrative health care looks for the answer to people's health in their own experiences and understandings of their lives. It taps into other innovative ideas of public health care such as personalisation, allowing a co-production between health workers and patient. The process delivers more successful and efficient health outcomes and higher patient satisfaction because it encourages a fuller and more nuanced sharing of information between doctor and patient.[85]

A similar approach has been developing within one part of Glasgow, where NHS mental health professionals have collaborated with library managers and librarians from Glasgow City Council using bibliotherapy. People accessing GPs and other health services are referred not necessarily to medication and other traditional treatment methods, but instead to self-help books and support groups as a less intrusive and more human way of sharing stories, learning from others and getting better.[86] The 'Healthy Reading' scheme, which is the first of its kind in Scotland, has been set up by NHS Greater Glasgow's South-East Psychosocial Services (STEPS), in liaison with Glasgow City Council and East Renfrewshire Council and has the additional effect of encouraging the use of public libraries, and an expansion of their functions.

TALES OF THE CITY. If storytelling is intimately bound up with what makes us human, then cities have a comparably distinguished association. According to Lewis Mumford's *The City in History*, the idea of the city contains the universal archetype of what it means to be human.[87] The city, for Mumford, has both a sense of the masculine and feminine, of rational power and order, and nurturing and caring for its citizens. Christopher Booker has also explored the way that cities bring together a mixture of classes and groups ranging from those 'above the line' to those 'below the line'.[88] All those who belong to a city are potentially enlarged by the sense of being part of a mighty organism much greater than any of its constituent parts. In this sense it is not surprising that all the way through the history of storytelling we see the city itself symbolising the archetype of the 'self', as 'the centre', the place where heroes and heroines can realise their full human potential. Many works of fiction are tales of people finding themselves in an urban setting, from Dick Whittington to *Sex in The City*.

Cities then are natural generators for stories — we need to create stories to help make sense of the world around us and to find our place in it. This can be seen across a number of different dimensions of the city, including the everyday city; part of the service; artists, singers and writers; urban media; digital stories; the folklore of the city.

The everyday city:

As Michel de Certeau put it, 'The story begins at ground level with footsteps'.[89] Laced through the routines of city life — where we walk, catch the metro, wait for a bus, pause at the watercooler and stand in line at the checkout — people open up 'pockets of interaction' chatter and trade stories with friends, colleagues and sometimes strangers.[90] The public spaces between and within buildings are where we see who we live with, what they look like and what they do. Whether we are frustrated or delighted by what we encounter often forms the content of stories we tell later at the bar or the dinner table.

According to the Glasgow City Council website, Glasgow is known as the friendliest city in the world,[91] and much of the everyday stories are traded in the city's unique vernacular known as 'the patter', made famous in Stanley Baxter's guide to the local tongue, *Parliamo Glasgow*[92] and the best-selling guide *The Patter*.[93]

Part of the service:

Storytelling is part of the service in urban life. If you want a feel for a place, taxi-drivers are a good place to start. Hairdressers, pub landlords, market traders and café shop owners aren't paid to tell you stories, but experiencing their services would not be the same without them.

Artists, singers and writers:

' It's a rain dirt town job hurts but it don't pay
All these calls they're making me and driving you insane
Don't you see
Don't you understand
Waiting for the phone to ring to make me all I am
You're in the suburbs waiting for somewhere to go
I'm down here working on some dumb show.'
— Deacon Blue, *Raintown*, 1987 [94]

' I walk across the rooftops
I follow a broken Thread
Of white rags falling slowly down
Flags caught on the fences.'
— The Blue Nile, *A Walk Across the Rooftops*, 1984 [95]

' Yes I know the city like a lover
Good or bad it's hard to love another that I've found
This is no mean town, no mean city.'
— Maggie Bell, No Mean City
(Theme Tune to *Taggart* TV series), 1983 [96]

Entire professions, art forms and ways of life have
emerged around telling the story of the city in the
twentieth century — from LS Lowry's depictions of
Salford in the 1920s, to New York's socially conscious
hip-hop in the 1980s. What the comedians, musicians
and writers create from the urban environment in turn
informs the stories told by people in the city.

The richness of the story-making power of cities is illuminated in Glasgow. It is a city that feels bigger and more resonant than the physical space it inhabits. In this, Glasgow, like other cities, exists both in reality and as an imagined city of the mind. In her wonderful study of 200 years of the Glasgow novel, Moira Burgess writes about 'drawing a map of fictional Glasgow to be laid over the real map, so that we can see where the two cities match and where they diverge'.[97] These are some of the numerous ways in which stories are represented.

THE CITY OF LITERATURE: From 1930s novel *No Mean City*, which portrayed the city as a place of razor gangs and thugs to William McIlvanney's *Laidlaw*, which he later claimed the TV series *Taggart* was taken from, to Alasdair Gray's *Lanark* and the work of James Kelman and Janice Galloway.

THE CITY IN DOCUMENTARY: Film documentaries such as *Glasgow 1980* (1971), and *Seawards the Great Ships* (1961) celebrated industrial traditions and modernist dreams. Later TV documentaries such as *World in Action*, *TV Eye* and *Panorama* portrayed Glasgow as a grim city of decline, and violence.

THE CITY IN FILM: The city has provided a rich backdrop to a host of films ranging from Bill Forsyth's comic portrayal of Glasgow East End wide boys, *That Sinking Feeling* (1980), to Ken Loach's exploration of race and identity in modern Glasgow in *Carla's Song* (1996), to Andrea Arnold's *Red Road* (2006), which depicts life through CCTV cameras in the infamous Red Road flat complex.

THE CITY IN TV DRAMA AND COMEDY
Glasgow's famous TV shows include *Rab C. Nesbitt* — set in deepest Govan — featuring Rab and his wife Mary Doll, *Tutti Frutti*, *River City* and *Taggart* — Scottish Television's famous detective series — which has long outlived its hero.

THE CITY IN THEATRE
The city has thrown up a range of playwrights ranging from the work of Clyde Unity Theatre in the 1930s to such plays as *The Steamie*, the oft-repeated *The Gorbals Story*, John Byrne's *The Slab Boys Trilogy* and, in 1990, the ambitious *The Ship*.

THE CITY IN MUSIC
Glasgow in song covers a range of emotions – from the melancholy of the Blue Nile's *A Walk Across the Rooftops*, to the theme tune of *Taggart*, *I Know the City Like a Lover*. From the 1980s stadium rock of songs like *Raintown* (Deacon Blue) and *Waterfront* (Simple Minds) to the more recent melodies of Belle and Sebastian and Franz Ferdinand.

THE CITY IN PHOTOGRAPHY
The city's changing shape, feel and look of its people has been chronicled in photos in the *Herald* and *Evening Times*. The most famous chronicler of the city via the lens has been Oscar Marzaroli, whose black and white photographs of kids on the streets of Gorbals and motorways being built through the heart of the city are emblematic of the great changes Glasgow has been through. Today the strength of the city's amateur photographers can be seen by entering the 'Glasgow' in the photo sharing website, flickr.

Urban media:

' Snow Causes Chaos as Winter Blasts Glasgow'
' Man in Fight for Life after Stabbing'
' Charges over Grandmother's Death after Remains Found'
' Value of Glasgow's Homes Surge'
' Glasgow Designer Shop Ram Raider Guilty'
' Glasgow Teachers Top List for Stress Days Off'
' Glasgow Ranked In World's Top 10 *Must See* Places'
— Headlines from *The Herald* and *Evening Times* (2007)

The news-based urban media provides the most naked form of commercial storytelling in cities, through paid-for newspapers, local radio and the free press. *The Evening Standard* is circulated to about half a million people daily in London, while the free *Metro* newspaper circulates to 1.1 million papers in predominantly urban areas across the UK.[98] Glasgow newspapers like the *Evening Times* and *the Herald* continue to be regarded as the voices and chroniclers of the city, read daily by many thousands of loyal readers. As the headlines opposite show, both these papers capture and promote a range of sometimes sensational images and stories about the city's fortunes and experiences and that of its inhabitants.

Digital stories:

The emergence of social software and Web 2.0 point to a range of new ways of mapping and constructing urban stories. Wikipedia enables anyone with a computer and an internet connection to write the history, politics, culture and gossip of any city or place in the world. 'Tagging' and now 'geo-tagging' on sites like flickr enable anyone to amass and view photos of places.
Most significantly blogs — and networks of different bloggers based in cities — present an entirely new way to listen to stories about urban living. At the time of writing there are 151 bloggers listed as from Glasgow on the Scottish Blogs website,[99] blogging on everything from being a vicar in Glasgow,[100] to living as a Canadian in Glasgow,[101] to a life campaigning for the Scottish National Party.[102]

The folklore of the city:

Every city at different points in history develops its own folklores. These explain a city's origins, its initial growth, its changing geography and geometric logic, its evolving economic, social and cultural mix, and its connections to the wider world via trade, emigration and other links. These get distilled into a collection of inherited stories, some over-romanticised, longing for a golden age that never was. But they all live on and help frame the present and future development.

EMPIRE CITY

'The second city of the Empire': Glasgow — or its wealthy parts — prospered massively through the age of Empire, and in particular its Victorian peak. It expanded in size, population and found itself at the nexus of a series of international networks of trade, commerce and wealth.

A WORKERS' CITY

This is a city shaped by the power and size of its working classes at the point when the city's manufacturing, steel, shipping and coal, dominated the economy. Glasgow is dominated by class, and the sense of power inherent in the collective nature of the working classes.

RIVER CITY

'The Clyde made Glasgow and Glasgow made the Clyde': the Clyde was the city's gateway to the world and brought the world to Glasgow. At one point, a quarter of the world's shipps were made on the banks of the Clyde, as well as the 'Queen Mary' and 'Queen Elizabeth' liners.

GANGLAND GLASGOW

This is a city scarred and marked by violence, gangs and high levels of crime and violence: 'the murder capital of Europe'. This version of Glasgow has been given powerful mileage by

o *Mean City*, TV, film and media reportage — and to some
xternal observers — remains the dominant image of the city.

IVIDED CITY

ual identity has been one of the main ways commentators
tempt to understand Scottish identity — and Glasgow has been
ven more shaped by this. The city has been scarred by divisions
ong the lines of religion, Protestant versus Catholic, football
d poverty. With its proximity to Northern Ireland, at the height
f the troubles Glasgow was called by some of the media 'Belfast
ithout the bombs'.

GALITARIAN CITY

lasgow for all its inequalities has prided itself on being a city
f the commonwealth — a city lacking in deference towards
uthority or those who think they are better. It has illustrated
ese qualities in its humour, public houses, and left-wing
olitics, from the early days of the Labour Party to the 1971
pper Clyde Shipworkers' sit-in, when the workers at five
ipyards staged a sit-in, in opposition to their mooted closure.

From storytelling to a futures-literate city

The storytelling richness of cities is clear. The opportunity
and challenge is whether this capability can be used to
understand better not just the past and the present, but
also the shared futures of cities — at the individual and
collective level.

It is axiomatic to state that the future is uncertain
and inherently unpredictable. As any self-respecting
futures analyst will admit, the world of predictions is a
risky game. Even the most illustrious can come unstuck.
The Hudson Institute's comprehensive *The Year 2000*,
published in 1967, sought to predict the last third of the
twentieth century. Among many omissions it missed the

growth of environmental imperatives, the emergence of the Middle East as an area of instability, and the rise of Islam.[103]

We will never hold in our hands a crystal ball that can unlock the secrets of tomorrow. However, thinking about the future can be constructive and valuable. It can help one make better decisions in the present, mindful of the full range of possibilities that the future might hold.

Individuals have the power to shape their environments effectively and responsibly, but too often are paralysed by fear about how to manage change. The concept of futures literacy is based on the premise that by enabling people to create and consider a range of alternative futures in a safe but challenging way, we can get ourselves 'unstuck' from the assumptions we hold about the present and find the confidence to act in the here and now. It is fundamentally tied to notions of having capacity and confidence in the present, and a belief in human agency. It is about democratising the present and the future through opening up authorship and assumptions about what kinds of futures are possible, probable and preferred.

Glasgow 2020 set out to conduct a mass public imagination experiment using storytelling to explore the appetite and ability of people to engage in futures literacy. We wanted to see if there was the potential for people to be able to tell their own more compelling stories about the city and its possible, probable and preferred futures than the restricted menu on offer from the official future.

THE STORIES

Glasgow 2020 set out with a belief in the power and importance of story — as a way to develop mass imagination, to contribute towards the reimagining of Glasgow and the articulation of a non-institutional view of the city, and to further the understanding and practice of futures literacy. The project developed its support for story and story creation in a number of ways:

- Glasgow 2020 events encouraged participants to create characters who lived in the city in the future, to sketch out elements of their life, and to shape these into embryonic storylines.
- From this, storymakers took away the resulting materials and used them as a starting point to make a story of the city in the future.
- Two short-story competitions were run: one with Glasgow University Creative Writing course and the other city-wide in association with the Evening Times.

The following 11 stories come from different contexts: some from Glasgow 2020 workshops and public events from which authors created stories, and some from the various public competitions. Authors represented here include published writers, emerging ones and those just starting out. They are collected here not as predictions of the future, nor as a representations of specific views of people during the project, but to show the potency, power and range of material and experience drawn on by storywriters to create their imagined worlds. They are printed here, unedited as they are written.

The stories cannot be squeezed into executive summaries or policy prospectuses. This is a world that has to be entered, experienced and inhabited.

THAT CHANGE IS NOTHING

— Ewan Gault

Jack McGurn squeezed his legs through the railings and let his feet swing above the Kelvin. He rested his head against the cold metal sweat and wished he had some stale rolls to throw at the ducks. Jack was not in a good mood. His designer jacket stank of smoke and someone had spilt red wine down the lapel. He wasn't far from the flat that he shared with his wife, or the Fat Controller as he called her, but was afraid that the someone getting the blame for the wine stain would be him.

He shivered. Dawn was clapping her cold hands to his face, sneaking them down his back when he wasn't looking. The Fat Controller wouldn't be leaving for work until this evening and with only shrapnel, a sketchbook, broken pencil and lump of tissue paper fossilised by a trip through the wash in his pockets there was little chance of getting out of the cold. Wearily he tried to join the dotted memories of last night's discussion with other artists, idlers and cinematography makers in which the future had been saved, destroyed, then saved again.

The river toiled and troubled below, keeping the ducks bobbing up and down the slower side water. A mallard standing on a rock observed him with tilted head curiosity.

'You're not going to jump?'

'No way pal. It's not high enough.'

The mallard quacked a joke with his friends who continued paddling ferociously up the same stretch again and again. If he was a duck he'd just let himself go.

Jack began walking towards Kelvin Bridge, hoping that he'd find a café open at this early hour. The trees were malting burnt butterfly swarms of leaves and Jack had a strange notion that it would be nice to be buried under a great pile of them.

On Kelvin Bridge Jack pretended not to see an old jakey holding up the chewed rim of a polystyrene cup. The man watched him through watery eyes looking hurt, angry, depressed. Whatever works best. Jack noticed the man's skin the colour of inner city lichen and looked a little disgusted, shocked, deaf. Whatever works best. He held his change tightly in case it rattled him. The Underground sighed softly as he approached and he smiled as he felt its disinfected breath.

'Change?'

The word echoed in Jack's head. He felt the money in his clenched fist and thought he probably had enough for an Underground ticket, a day spent dozing round the clockwork orange.

Jack rushed down to the platform to hear the train groaning down the tunnel so sad to have missed him. 'Not to worry,' he shouted, 'I'm in no hurry.' He began whistling the silence away and wished he could tap dance. Faintly he heard the howl of a distant train and the underground air began snaking around his ankles. It seemed unusual that one train should follow another so quickly but it meant the carriage was empty and that without embarrassing himself Jack could stretch out, rest his cheek on the seats' multi-browned material that had absorbed all the farts and fidgets of the city. As he drifted he recalled a friend's theory that the Underground's trains were designed to rattle to prevent people from falling asleep and missing their stop.

When Jack awoke the train was full of passengers who kept sneaking up and prodding him with their eyes. He felt wonderfully comfortable and was intent on turning over and chasing the tail of a dream when he was poked with an umbrella. A women with an aged ballerina's face peered at him making a clucking noise. All the passengers were dressed in sharply cut business suits, stroking and patting the briefcases on their laps. The rush hour he thought attempting and failing to recognise his reflection in the ghost carriage through the window. People sat contemplating their fingernails as if they had never seen them before. Jack took out his sketchbook and was about to do a few quick portraits but was horrified to see the gnarled, yellow claws coming out of his own fingers. He could hear the Fat Controller's scolding voice and wondered how he had gone so long without cutting them. He made his hands into fists, half closed his eyes and watched the passengers, their cases a polished shine, their faces creased and tough. The train stopped at St George's Cross and Jack realised that if this was the rush hour at the end of the day as opposed to the start he could soon go home.

'Excuse me, extremely sorry to bother you,' he croaked, as if he hadn't spoken in years. The passengers facing him became even more fascinated in their fingernails apart from one young fellow who grinned. 'I was just wondering if you had a watch?'

'A watch? No haven't had one of them in years.'

'Well do you know the time, I mean roughly, is it say nine o'clock in the morning or five at night?'

The man laughed, stuck his finger in his ear and whispered, 'Time please.' He looked at Jack and said, 'It's 5.24.' Jack tried not to stare but the man appeared to have a small electronic headphone attached to his ear.

'Next you'll be telling me you don't know what year it is.'

'Ehm, 2005,' Jack said, pulling a stupid face.

'Aye try 2020.'

They both laughed and Jack leaned back. After a bit he found himself peering over the shoulder of the elderly chap to his right. The man was reading an electronic book, which seemed to contain various stories and pictures on a screen that was soft to the eye like paper. It made Jack shudder to see a man old enough to be his father at ease with technology he hadn't even heard of. He tried to read the story, which appeared to be a news item, and having caught the words Oil, War, America and Greed felt somewhat reassured. As the train slipped into Buchanan Street the elderly gentleman gave Jack a superior look and pressed a button on his machine, which let out an angry rustle of paper. Jack looked away embarrassed and thought that now would be a good time to alight.

As he got to his feet Jack's knees creaked 'Not this again.' He ambled in a most unseemly manner whispering fierce little commands to his bones to stop their moans and groans. I really have to take more care of myself he thought, whilst resting against the clammy tile wall. As the train rushed into a blur he imagined noticing that each carriage was of a different type; one brightly decorated, full of soft hanging toys and screaming weans, the next four filled with wheel chairs and nurses, wizened old dears clutching support bars. The last carriage was covered in a web of graffiti that looked like it had been spun by a spider on acid. Inside wane young faces and the peaks and troughs of multi-coloured hair ranges began to nod as the train disappeared into darkness. Jack listened to it slither down the tunnel and realised that the reason he had slept so comfortably was that this train hadn't sounded like some arthritic rattlesnake but had been smooth, silent, streamline.

He strode up the scales of the escalator and thought he noticed the CCTV cameras exchanging winks, whispering about him, behind his back. He was carried past a strange map in which the clockwork orange had sprouted legs.

Buchanan Street smelt of vinegar and breweries. Jack took a deep breath and felt at home. Out of the Underground his first mission was to find a toilet. Other than visiting a few well-worn pubs he only ever went to the city center on what he called guerrilla-shopping missions during which he peeled his gaze from the shops' shiny fronts and let his eyes clamber upon the grand old buildings above. He stood there wondering where he could find a toilet when he noticed that a nearby church spire had a rash of satellite dishes attached to it. Intrigued he moved closer and noticed that in place of the times of service was the name of a telecommunications company. Jack was not a religious person but still felt a little scandalised by this. He started ambling towards Sauchiehall Street wondering what his arty friends would make of a building once used to direct man's thoughts towards God now being used to allow us to talk to each other.

He found his eyes drawn to the glowing embers of adverts beamed down to him from the screen above the Concert Hall. As his gaze nipped round the corner he realised that there was more than just one of these screens. There were loads of them. Jack looked around, trying to catch someone's eye, to share a shrug that would say 'What's this all about then?' But nobody seemed up for it. He caught himself making a face at a group of shop window mannequins who stared back with dull opaque eyes. They looked in need of a good feed, impossibly sharp cheekbones and cruel elbows. They were certainly the skinniest mannequins he had ever seen and he wasn't quite sure which ones were meant to be boys that looked like girls and which ones girls that looked like boys.

He thought that there must be toilets in the clothes shops but was a little afraid of these trendy places. Sauchiehall Street though was filled with busy cafés; well-dressed groups huddled round coffees under large steel heaters. Jack could feel their warmth. He had a few pounds left which would surely get him a drink and allow him to legitimately use a toilet. After passing a couples of places Jack selected one in which the manager's ambition to have as attractive and short skirted a staff as possible had been perfectly realised. Jack weaved his way between the tables smiling at one of the girls. She looked up and dropped her tray, shock on her bright little face.

'What, what?'

He knew his suit was a little crumpled, that he was perhaps a bit bleary eyed but this. Jack found his hand rising to rub his face, an action he often did when embarrassed and felt long, straggly, matted hair.

'Please, Sir, no trouble, no trouble please. But I really must insist that you leave the premises.'

Jack held out his cupped hands, showing the manager his money.

'No sir, this will not do. That money is no longer legal currency. If you do not leave I will have my staff accompany you.'

Jack looked over the man's shoulder. Sure enough there were two large men, their faces looking strangely criminal when compared to the cafés customers. Jack turned and walked. Scratched his face. His beard! He had never had one of these before but found that it was a constant source of fascination to his claws. He picked and scratched, flattened it and fluffed it out. It appalled him really but how had it happened? He looked at his clothes, his suit

trousers were worn at the knee, and the buckle on the belt that his wife had bought for him was rusty. He remembered the joke that the man on the underground had made about it being 2020.

'How long have I slept?' He felt like he had fallen into the middle of a Fairy Tale.

Jack scuttled along staring at the paving. The going wasn't easy but people seemed to be good at keeping out of his path. He stopped outside a bookshop to check his reflection. He looked at a skull going bald, on top a few greasy strands smeared over like a bar code. His beard went down past the collar of his once smart suit which now had the dusty, sweat drenched look of an item that had been in hiding in the darkest corners of a charity shop.

He pushed on the shop's front door. There were people inside and it was clearly doing business but the door appeared locked. He tried pulling, had a go at the other door but neither was a success. He started scratching his beard. There was a strange little box next to the door and he watched a lady take a card from her purse and swipe it. She waited, humming and tapping her foot until the door beeped open. Jack slipped in behind her before it had time to lock. A security guard stopped him.

'If you haven't swiped your credit card, I'm afraid you can't enter.'

'Sorry, I didn't know, but I really must use your toilet.'

'I can't allow that. It's more than my job's worth.'

'But you don't understand. I know I look a state but I'm really quite well off. It's just that I fell asleep on the underground in 2005 and woke up like this.'

The Security Guard bit his lower lip and looked over his shoulder.

'Go on then.'

Jack wanted to hug him but doubted the man would appreciate it. Instead he muttered many thanks and moved stealthfully to the toilets, his hand stuffed deep in his pockets for fear that someone would think he was a thief. Jack left the shop with something approaching a spring in his stride. Although the bathroom mirror had shown the effects of the fifteen years he had spent asleep, Jack felt that with a hair cut, a shave and some decent clothes he could look quite distinguished. He had managed to bum a fag off the Security Guard who had said all the best and he had God blessed him and all the rest. Now all he had to do was get home.

Sauchiehall Street had been pedestrianised all the way to Charing Cross with young trees planted in a line down the middle of the street. Jack was enjoying walking on the clean pavement looking at the fashion changes that weren't new so much as updated versions of styles that were fashionable years ago. He realised that his array of New Romantic ruffle shirts and pirate hats that the Fat Controller had exiled to the attic would now be very desirable. He felt vaguely smug about this and lit the cigarette taking a long hungry draw. The smoke stung the back of his throat and he doubled up coughing and wheezing for breath. An alarm went off above his head and a light started flashing. After fifteen years the nicotine hit was a bit much and he retched his head between his knees. When he looked up two luminous coated policewomen were striding down the street.

'Well, what do we have here?'

'Ehm, I've not smoked for a wee while and it sort of got to me.'

'Do you realise that your smoke set off this alarm?'

Jack shook his head.

'And that it's illegal to smoke anywhere in the city centre?'

Jack looked confused.

'Well, where have you been for the past decade?'

Jack didn't think they would believe him.

A Police Van nudged its way through pedestrians and he was bundled in the back.

'We can't have your sort cluttering up the city centre. Now, where can we take you?'

'Kelvin Bridge.'

'And you have a place where you can stay?'

'Yes. Well, I think so.'

They drove off. Stopping at lights on Charing Cross. Jack for once realised that he missed his wife and hoped she would be at home to scold him. He looked up at the familiar buildings, at two stone babies reclining above a shop door. Their sculpted smiles and dusty eyes had seen it all before. They watched the rush and go, the stop and flow of the streets.

'Nobody stays here long.'

They hold onto a great white-faced clock as if they might fall. Its hands are stuck at twelve. They've been that way for years.

On Woodlands and Great Western Road, Jack notices small changes to shop fronts; cars are smaller, some solar panelled. The reassuring thing is that all the buildings look exactly the same. He remembers looking at photos of nineteenth century Glasgow in one of his favourite pubs and how easy it was to recognise the two spires of the churches on Great Western Road, the long line of tenements looking like the road had been carved through them rather than that they had been built up around the road.

Jack got dropped off at Kelvin Bridge. He looked towards where his old tenement flat had been and saw a brand new building, all white walls and glass balconies. He leaned over the side of the bridge and felt sick.

'You're naw gonnae jump?' Asked an old man with watery eyes.

'Nah, probably not, though I could do with the wash.' The man grinned. 'What do they call that then?'

'That's Kelvin Quay. Put it up a few years ago.'

'Used to be tenements there.'

'Aye terrible bother wi subsidence, pulled them aw down.' Jack nodded, remembering the strange angles of the walls and doorframes in his old flat, how the Underground trains would rattle the windows, and stir his dreams.

The man said good night and tucked himself tight against the night. Jack thought of all the old mobile numbers that he only half knew, of the addresses of friends that had probably moved. People hurried past, each with a place to go, a person to be with. He felt cold to the bone and went to stand at the Underground's entrance.

It panted the same hot breath, same

disinfected smell. Jack slithered down the railings and sat facing the open mouth, the escalator tongue. He watched only legs and feet. He didn't think he would recognise anyone and didn't want anyone to recognise him. He picked up an empty polystyrene cup, held in between his palms as if it might warm him.

'Change,' he found himself whispering. 'Change?'

Ewan Gault graduated from the University of Glasgow with an MA in creative writing in 2006. He was recently awarded the Fish-Knife Award for Crime Short-Fiction. 'That Change is Nothing' was the main prizewinner in the Glasgow 2020 competition for Glasgow University Creative Writing Masters course students.

†

GROWING WILD

— Jeanette Stafford

Footsteps followed me along the dark street. I walked faster and the footsteps accelerated likewise. I turned down a side road, hoping that I was imagining things. The tenement houses were dark and quiet, their sightless windows offering no comfort. I hurried past the rusting hulk of a huge four wheel drive, its prestige value now even lower than the availability of the fuel to power it. Still the footsteps followed.

Suddenly an arm grabbed me and a hand went over my mouth.

'Stay still and keep quiet and you'll be okay.'

The voice was familiar but I couldn't place it. My instinct was to struggle and yell, but the arms held me immobile, pulling me into the shadows of a tenement doorway. The footsteps which had been following went past, paused after a few meters, crossed over and faded into the distance.

The person holding me let out a sigh and loosened his grip and I spun round to face a tall skinny man with straggly hair.

'Jake! What the hell are you doing? You scared me!'

'Some gratitude that is!' he sulked. 'You could've been in real trouble there. Christ knows what kind of creep wis followin' you.'

'I can take care of myself, thanks,' I said. 'What do you think you are, a guardian angel or something?'

'Aye, well, I quite the fancy the position if it's free,' he joked. 'Anyway, what the bloody hell are you doing out at this time of night, on yer own? Don't you know there's a curfew?'

'Of course I know. I went to find these,' I said, holding up the two rabbits I had retrieved, still in their snares.

'Bloody hell, Marion, what are ye goney dae with them?'

'Plant them in the garden!' I said, watching his expression as he struggled to work out whether I was serious.

'Look,' he said, 'Ah think we're takin' a

chance out here. There's somewhere we can stay till it gets light.'

He pushed open the outer door of the close, pulled out a huge bunch of keys and opened the front door to one of the flats on the ground floor. A gust of stale air met us as he pulled me inside and shut the door.

'Whose house is it?' I asked, wondering about his key collection.

'Some poor bugger that bit the dust a few months back,' he replied. 'There's no family as far as Ah know so Ah kept hold of the key. Thought it might come in handy.'

I hesitated.

'It's alright, there's no dead bodies lying about. The sanitary have been in an' cleaned it up. Ah know, because it was one o' mine. They left me tae lock up after.'

He jangled the keys and I presumed he had acquired the rest in the same manner.

'How come you're trusted with them?'

He lit a candle then led the way to the kitchen where I deposited the rabbits and he rummaged in cupboards for some form of sustenance.

'Not trusted exactly,' he said. 'Let's say Ah forgot tae hand them in.'

He found a can of Tennent's and pulled the tab.

'Last one Ah'm afraid. Want a slug?'

I shook my head. I would have boiled the kettle but the power was off so I settled for a drink from the tap.

'So what's Tommy's wee sister doing out at this time with two deid rabbits then?' he asked. 'Don't you join the queue at Asda with yer ration book like everybody else round here?'

'That's a mug's game,' I said in disgust. 'There's plenty of food out there if you know where to look for it.'

He screwed up his face in puzzlement. 'Like what for instance?'

'All sorts,' I said, but before I could enlighten him there was a frantic hammering at the door.

'Shite,' he said. 'Don't tell me somebody's cliped on us. Stay where you are and don't make a sound.'

He went to the front door and looked through the spy hole which the previous occupant had installed. He opened the door and dragged in a small scruffy man, closing and bolting the door behind him.

'Andy! How did you know Ah wis here? Ah hope naebody followed you!'

'Don't be daft! I made sure they didnae. Let's jist say it wus a lucky guess.'

Andy wiped blood from his nose and sweat from his forehead.

'What the hell happened to you? You're in some state, man!'

'Bloody Rab's gang,' he panted. 'Tried tae find where I keep the fuel. I managed tae leg it before they did too much damage, but they'll no' give up.'

'Well if they turn up here you're on yer own, sunshine. I don't want any trouble frae that bunch o' nutters.'

'Okay, I get the picture. I'm sure I managed tae shake them aff afore I headed here.'

Andy flopped down in the hallway but Jake made him move through to the back room away from the door. He jumped when he saw me having assumed that Jake was alone.

'I hope I'm no' interruptin' anything,' he said with a leer.

'No, you're not,' I assured him. 'Are you alright?' I asked pointing to the blood stains on his shirt and bruises beginning to show on his face.

'Why were they after you?'

'They want tae control anything that's profitable around here and that includes my wee petroleum business,' he said.

Andy had been well known as a drug dealer, peddling death around Glasgow's ghettos and funding his own privileged lifestyle from other people's misery. His income dried up overnight when the Government legalised all drugs including heroin and he had been obliged to find an alternative source of employment. However Andy was a jammy beggar and when one commodity lost its scarcity value another one trundled along to provide him with a brand new opportunity.

An engine revved nearby and Jake pinched the candle flame and ducked below window height. He indicated us to follow suit and Andy and I both dived to the floor, just in time as the curfew patrol passed shining lights in windows as they went by.

'Try and get some sleep,' Jake suggested. 'Marion, you have one of the beds in the other room an' me an' Andy'll stay here.'

'No thanks,' I said. 'I don't fancy kipping where some stranger snuffed it, even if you did clean the place up. I'll stay here too. This chair will do fine.'

The thought of spending the rest of the night alone in a strange room which had seen the dreaded flu at its worst didn't appeal to me at all, and besides, I wanted to keep an eye on the other two. Jake was an old friend of my brother's and I could almost trust him, but Andy was another matter altogether. I pulled a travel rug over my knees and tried to get comfortable.

I hadn't meant to sleep, but I must have dozed off and was wakened in the early light by clattering and banging coming from the kitchen. I went to investigate and found Andy searching for food.

'Baked beans, tomato soup or cling peaches,' he said. 'What's yer preference madam?'

He was trying to raise a smile but I did not feel like obliging.

'Baked beans will do fine,' I said. 'Give me the tin, unless you want some yourself.'

'Cold beans,' he pulled a face. 'No thanks. I'll have the peaches. It's bloody freezin' in here. Can we no' get some heat? What about the fireplace in the other room? Could we light a fire d'ye think?'

'No way,' I said. 'There's nothing to burn and you've no idea if the chimney's swept. Set that on fire and we'll soon draw attention to ourselves.'

I could see that he was eyeing up some furniture with a view to using it as firewood. I did not want to be around if he did try to light a fire so I finished the beans, picked up the rabbits and let myself out into the cool morning air. I had not gone far when Jake caught up with me.

'You haven't left that head banger on his own in that flat have you?' I was not sure why the possibility worried me.

'No, of course Ah huvny,' he said. 'Ah turfed him out and told him tae get lost.'

'Why do you hang around with scum like him, anyway?' I asked.

'It's a long story,' he replied. 'You're no' too keen on him ur ye? D'ye still blame him fur whit happened tae Tommy?'

'Yes, I do,' I said. 'I'll never forgive him for that.'

My brother had been one of Andy's gang when he was younger and had become addicted to heroin. He would have died of an overdose one night if I hadn't been there when he stopped breathing. I had struggled to resuscitate him but had somehow managed to keep him alive until the paramedics came. The memory was still raw.

Jake kept pace with me as I headed for home.

'How is Tommy these days anyway? He is still with us I hope.'

'He's fine, as far as I know,' I reassured him. 'He went cold turkey a while ago, managed to avoid the curse of the methadone and he's stayed clean since. Now he's gone north to see if he can make a go of living on the croft. It belonged to our grandparents and Tommy thinks that self sufficiency will be the answer to all our problems. He's going to patch up the cottage, keep chickens and grow his own veg. He reckons if he keeps busy it'll help him stay off the hard stuff.'

'Why didn't you go with him? Isn't it lonely by yourself since yer ma an' da' both passed away?'

'I'm fine,' I didn't mean to sound quite so defiant. 'I've always lived here and I don't feel inclined to give up on the place simply because of a flu pandemic. Things will get better again soon, I'm sure.'

I was nearly home but I still had the rabbits to deal with. I paused at a low wall and pulled out my knife. Jake looked at me in alarm but his expression changed when I placed my kill on top and decapitated first one and then the other, then slit them from throat to tail, scooping out the entrails into the long grass. Jake looked as if he was about to throw up.

'Bloody hell, Marion,' he looked at me in disgust. 'Where did you learn to do that? It's bowfin'!'

'What a wimp!' I said. 'Have you never gutted fish? There's not much difference. You're too used to having your nice safe little hamburger delivered in a nice sterile polystyrene box. Not much chance of blood and guts in a Happy Meal, is there?'

'Okay, point taken,' he said, 'But Ah

think Ah'd rather join the queue at Asda with my ration book if that's the alternative. What a stink!'

I finished cleaning and skinning the rabbits, wiped my hands on the grass and headed for the tower block, Jake still in tow.

'How come you're so squeamish?' I asked. 'Surely you've encountered worse working with the sanitary?'

'No' really,' he replied. 'Most of the corpses were quite fresh an' all we had tae do was pack them intae body bags.'

'I suppose if you were working for them you must have had the flu then?'

'Aye. Everyone else in my family passed away. I'm the only one left. What about you, did you catch it?'

'No, but I nursed Mum and Dad and then Tommy. I suppose I must be immune for some reason. Tommy recovered when things were at their worst so that's why he went north. He didn't want to get called up for the sanitary crews — didn't fancy shifting bodies. I'm surprised that you're so public spirited.'

'Aye, well, I didnae huv much choice. We don't all huv a wee croft in the Highlands to escape to. Nane o' ma distant relatives left me a wee hoose an' a bit ground tae grow stuff. Those that dae are lucky.'

We passed a huge heap of stinking rubbish piled up in the car park and paused at the entrance of the tower block.

'Bye then,' I said and turned to go in, hoping that he would take the cue to leave but he said,

'Are ye no' goney ask me up fur a coffee, then, seein' Ah walked you home safely?'

I looked him straight in the eye and said, 'No, I'm not.'

'Ah'll see you around then, will Ah?' he looked hopeful but the only promise I wanted to make was, 'Not if I see you first.'

Soon after dawn the next day I was heading for the parkland when Jake appeared from nowhere. I suspected that he had been waiting for me and I wondered if I had acquired my very own stalker.

'Where are you off to in such a hurry?' he asked.

'Over there,' I said, pointing towards the mature trees in the distance. I pulled some twine from my pocket and he understood.

'Great,' he said, 'Ah'll come with ye an' make sure yer ok.'

'I'd rather go alone,' I said. 'Two people make a lot more noise than one and you never know who's going to be hanging about.'

'That's why I don't think you should go on yer own,' he said.

I stopped and glared at him. 'I don't need a bloody minder, thanks,' I said. 'I've been managing fine until now, in case you hadn't noticed. You'll only get in the way.'

He looked hurt and I felt really mean, especially since he had been my big brother's best mate.

'All right, come with me if you must,' I said, 'but keep your head down and shut up when I tell you to, and don't keep blethering!'

We walked in silence until we reached the woods. I made a small noose and attached it to a low branch with some sunflower seeds as bait then I led Jake to a clearing where a patch of wild raspberries glowed in the sunlight. I pulled an old pillowcase from the pocket of my army surplus jacket and started filling it with fruit. Jake tried to help, but he kept picking the unripe berries and I had to show him how to tell which ones to take and which to leave. When we had about half a kilo I made my way back to the tree where I had set my snare and found that a grey squirrel had obligingly hung itself in the noose. I freed its warm little body from the twine and slipped it into my pocket then reset the snare. This time I set off to find wild garlic and wild carrots but we hadn't gone far when there was a loud flapping from the direction of the tree. I rushed back to find a wood pigeon caught by the leg, struggling to free itself and becoming more and more frantic as the noose tightened.

I was terrified that the noise of the pigeon would attract an undesirable form of attention, so I climbed up, grabbed the bird and took its head between my fingers giving a sharp yank. The bird flapped madly then lay still and I slipped it into my other pocket.

'Bloody hell, Marion, what are you like?' Jake hissed.

I put my finger to my lips to tell him to be quiet. A twig snapped behind me and I turned round to see one of big Rab's gang standing in a shaft of sunlight grinning at me.

'Well, well, what have we here,' he said. 'Looks like Maid Marian an' Robin Hood tae me. Poachin'.'

He pointed to my bulging pockets.

'Looks like yous two are in big trouble now, dunntit?'

'Piss off,' I said. 'We've got as much right to be here as you do.'

'Aye, well, we'll see what Big Rab has tae say about that, will we,' and he made a grab for me. I ducked and squirmed out of the way, and Jake thumped him in the guts. Another thug came from behind to crack Jake across the jaw and a third one gave him a bloody nose. I hid in a rhododendron bush but then realised that Jake was outnumbered. I couldn't just leave him to it so I found a large branch and with the advantage of surprise, battered one of Rab's heavies over the skull with it, knocking him out cold. I rammed the second in the chest, winding him and tripped up the third, improving our odds to the point of escape. I grabbed Jake and we sprinted into the woods. We fled past the burned out ruins of the gallery, now looted and derelict, and down the driveway onto the main thoroughfare with its regular patrols of soldiers.

'Some guardian angel you are!' I said, panting. 'That's the first time I've ever taken anyone with me to the park and the first time I've ever got caught by Rab's gang!'

'Don't blame me!' he gasped. 'It was that stupid pigeon's fault, flapping about an' makin' all that racket!'

'At least we've still got something for dinner,' I said, 'but pudding's off.' The raspberries were still inside the pillowcase, tramped into the dust under the trees.

We managed to lose Rab's mates and I was nearly home when we spotted a body lying in the gutter. Jake, ever the Good Samaritan, went over to check whether the bloke was still breathing or not and gave a shout.

'Marion, come here, quick. It's Andy.'

The stupid bugger wasn't looking too hot. He was unconscious and there was a dribble of blood mixed with saliva coming from his lips. A Land Rover parked nearby had its petrol cap missing. There was a piece of tubing protruding from the tank and a half filled jerry can sitting on the pavement.

'Eejit!' said Jake. 'Forgot what he was on his knees for and swallowed instead of spitting. Now look at him. We canny leave him there. We'll have tae dae somethin'.'

I looked at Jake with disbelief, partly because it had never occurred to me that Andy the Glasgow hard man might be gay, but mostly because I would much rather have walked away than got involved in trying to help this particular chancer.

Jake shook him and he groaned then his muscles contracted in a spasm and he retched, vomiting a mixture of diesel and blood onto the tarmac. It stank.

'I don't think there's much we can do,' I said. 'He's too heavy for us to carry and I reckon he's a gonner anyway. All that diesel will rot his guts — he'll not last long.'

'Come off it!' Jake was furious. 'We can't walk away and leave him. Help me get him up.'

'And what if someone catches us? It's going to be hard explaining how he got his insides scrambled with diesel if he wasn't siphoning fuel. What if they think we were helping him? We'll all be locked up.'

'Never mind about that, gimme a hand!' Jake insisted, and for some strange reason, I did.

We managed to take an arm each and get Andy to his feet. With his weight supported he was just conscious enough to put one foot in front of the other and we made our way slowly and painfully towards the tower block. I was cursing Andy for choosing to perform his suicidal type of theft so close to where I lived when a patrol passed and one of the soldiers spotted us. The armoured car stopped and he called out to find out what was wrong with Andy.

'He's drunk,' I said, hoping that we were not close enough for them to smell the reek of diesel fumes. The soldier looked at me suspiciously.

'It's his birthday. Somebody gave him a bottle of whisky and he had it for breakfast.' I must have lied convincingly because they drove off towards the supermarket to supervise the next consignment of rations.

'That was close!' said Jake. 'Ah thought

we were in for it there.'

Andy was still breathing when we got to the lobby. We summoned the lift and thankfully the doors opened. The journey up to the tenth floor seemed to take forever and I was terrified that the power would go off and strand us between floors.

'Why the hell dae ye live away up here?' demanded Jake. 'How can ye no' live doon there like most sane folk? There's plenty o' hooses goin' beggin' an' ye wouldnae huv tae worry about the lift workin'.'

'I don't usually take the lift!' I retorted. 'I like living here because it's anonymous and there's a great view — I can see when it's safe to go out. I don't understand what possesses you to look after him. You'd think he was your brother.'

'Same Da' different Ma',' Jake enlightened me and his concern for Andy suddenly made sense.

Eventually the doors opened again. I found my key and let us in to the small flat. We plonked Andy on the settee with a bucket nearby.

'What are we going to do with him?' I asked.

'Dunno,' he said, 'we canny really take him tae casualty, can we? They'll ask too many awkward questions.'

'Too right they will,' I said. Andy moaned.

'We need tae dae somethin' fur him — got any painkillers?'

'I don't think painkillers are going to help,' I said.

'Maybe some milk wid help, or porridge, or somethin'. Whit dae you think?' suggested Jake.

'Maybe you're right,' I said, 'I'll have to go and see what I can get. You stay here and look after him, give him some water to drink and keep quiet till I get back.'

I took my ration book and went out. It was good to be on my own again with time to think. I had been quite content looking after myself and keeping out of bother and I was really scunnered at finding myself landed with not just one but two dead beats to take care of.

When I got home three hours later it sounded as if Freddie Mercury had been resurrected and was performing live in my flat.

'We will, we will rock you,' he sang as the beat pounded off the tarmac and bounced off the surrounding buildings, advertising Jake's presence to all around.

I took the stairs two at a time and confronted Jake.

'What to you think you're playing at?' I yelled, turning the music off. 'I told you to keep quiet. Now everyone knows that we're here!'

'Sorry hen, Ah didnae think o' that,' said Jake. 'Ah got bored an' rummaged in yer stuff. Ah hadnae heard that one fur years.'

I poured Andy a glass of milk and coaxed him to drink it. He managed a few sips.

'What kept you, anyway? You wur gone ages.'

'I got some stuff to make soup,' I said. 'I thought some broth might do Andy good. Why don't you get cleaned up while I cook?'

We were both still filthy after our encounter in the park, and Jake had dried blood all over his face.

'There should be some hot water if you want a shower, but don't be greedy. Make sure you leave some,' I said.

'Don't you want tae join me?' he asked, looking hopeful.

'What do you think?' I said, picking up a knife and chopping vegetables.

Half an hour later Jake reappeared, clean shaven, his long hair slicked back behind his ears.

'Do you want some?' I offered him a share from the pot on the stove.

'No thanks,' he said, wrinkling his nose, 'but Ah'll have some o' that when it's ready.' He pointed to the oven where a game casserole was braising slowly.

I ladled the soup into two bowls and sprinkled some chopped herbs on one, which I gave to Jake.

'Here,' I said, 'take this and give him a hand with it. Make sure he swallows some and doesn't slitter it over my good settee.'

Andy had recovered enough to sit upright and with Jake's help he managed to sup the broth slowly. He winced at the taste and I guessed that it was a long time since he had eaten anything so nourishing.

'Aw hen, that's mingin',' he croaked. 'Can ye no' jist gie me a fag instead. I'll be okay the morra.'

'You know you're not allowed to smoke in council property,' I said, 'and there's no way I'd put a naked flame anywhere near you right now. The soup will put a lining on your stomach and you'll recover quicker, that way I'll be shot of you sooner, so eat up.'

'Fair enough,' he said. 'I suppose you could've left me in the street.'

I finished my broth and went for a shower.

I was drying between my toes when I saw that the bathroom door had swung open and Jake was watching me. I pulled the towel round me and glared at him.

'What do you think you're playing at?' I asked.

'Just admiring the view,' he said. 'The last time Ah saw ye in the scud ye were a scrawny wee kid. Ye've changed a bit since then.'

I tried to push him out of the way to shut the door, but he caught my arm.

'Come on Marion,' he said, pulling at the towel, 'Andy's fine and the food will keep.'

I scowled at him, but his dark eyes twinkled back at me. Up close he smelled delicious. I let the towel slip and Jake kissed me, his soft lips cool against my face and neck. As he pulled me close I thought of Andy in the next room. The hemlock I put in his soup must have tasted bitter and yet he had finished the bowl. Soon the poison would paralyse him, starting at his legs and working its way up his body until it reached his diaphragm. Then he would suffocate, slowly.

Normally I would dispatch an injured animal as quickly as possible, but with Andy, I made an exception.

Jeanette Stafford was the joint main prize winner in the Glasgow 2020 Story Writing Competition. 'Growing Wild' is her second published short story.

†

THE ICARUS TREE

— Suhayl Saadi

To Albert Ayler

Darkness and heat covered everything, but from the darkness, came chanting. A woman in her late twenties burst into the chamber, tripped over the leg of a large, rectangular table and fell headlong. On the table was a storm-lantern, an ashtray, a half-empty bottle of liquor and a crumpled-up newspaper. A man emerged from the shadows and lit the lantern and with it, a slim cigar. His face seemed to Leila to be obscenely long, the skin, smooth, waxy, yet the hint of a beard hovered around his jowl and his eyes gleamed like sapphires. In pin-stripes and with a tightly-knotted red tie, he looked thirty-five, maybe forty. The floor felt rough and warm beneath her cheek. She could see her dishevelled reflection in his shoes. Just as she got her breath back, he crouched down and blew smoke into her face. As she coughed, the chanting subsided. The walls of the oval room were covered with WW2-era ads — the big blonde faces, the bound-back hair, the concentrated gaze at infinity, the etiolated glimmer against the sky of anti-aircraft guns — but she noticed in the murk of the back wall, a full-sized, framed reproduction of what looked like a Dutch master.

Mind if I smoke? he smiled. His voice was pitched deep.

Leila got up. The chamber was around seven metres high and twenty in diameter and the door through which Leila entered now seemed to have vanished into the long shadows cast by the lantern.

These pictures…from my great-grand-mother's time.

Leila shuddered, though it must have been over ninety degrees. She lifted the lank, black strands out of her eyes. The chanting had faded away.

How far down is this?

He laughed.

Drink? Smoke…?

Leila's head began to pound as she tried to remember.

I was running. But first, I was walking.

Walking, running? Do you even know who you are?

I am Leila Morris, born twenty-...

He imitated her.

I am Leila Morris.

He was close now, his breath seared her skin. She closed her eyes. A familiar scent, difficult to place. He spoke so quietly, she thought she might be imagining it.

You are dancing, remember?

He began to hum a World War Two tune, circling his cigar through the air. Eyes still closed, Leila found her spine beginning to follow his movements as though he was a snake-charmer and she, a serpent. Shadows waltzed around the room.

You are dancing, slowly, languorously, in a park by the banks of the old river. All around you, the city.

He was behind her.

Through the branches of dead trees, the evening sunlight cuts across your skin. Yet you are far away.

I was walking through a summer wood, and the night was coming down, the trees, pressing in. I am trying to run. There is something behind me.

The chamber smelled of desiccation, as though like an Egyptian tomb for aeons it had remained sealed to the outside world.

Leila wiped the back of her neck.

Faster, faster I run until the leaves become bricks and I am in a tunnel, going down...

He broke in.

You remind me of a woman I once knew.

He ran his finger along the line of her eyebrows.

Shuffled cards with her during the war. Can't remember which war.

Leila twisted away. Yazid was wistful.

She was born in the forest, in a bed of leaves by a smoking mill.

He shifted his cigar into his left hand and extended his right.

Yazid, card shark, stock trader, general animal.

Leila did not take his hand and began to explore the chamber. She flicked through the newspaper. He let his arm fall and tipped ash onto the floor. Her voice frayed.

How did you get here, Yazid?

I was strolling through the tamed, deciduous countryside, aye, through the forest where long ago some king had his eye taken out.

He laughed, a strangely feminine laugh.

Through the assonant song of the brown thrush or the red breast or the blue tit, I came upon a door in the ground. At the centre of the door was a large brass ring. I knelt and pulled. Everything was light.

For the first time he seemed discomfited, his movements, jerky, uncertain. From his jacket, he took out a paper, carefully folded it, then removed a silver phial, unscrewed the top and tipped a small amount of white powder into the fold. Closing one nostril, he threw his head back and snorted, thrice. He put away paper and phial, smoothed back his hair and straightened out the soft cotton of his suit. He re-lit his cigar and brought out a pack of silver-backed playing cards which he began to shuffle. Through the cigar smoke, that scent again. Still puffing away, he fanned out the pack. Tentatively, she ventured a hand.

Yazid grabbed her wrist and pulled her closer. Suddenly, two people entered the chamber. One was in police uniform and she strode towards Yazid and yanked the cigar out of his mouth.

No smoking down here, sir.

She threw down the cigar and crushed it with the heel of her boot.

Gases.

Embarrassed, Leila drew back her hand. Yazid sneered.

And who are you? A canary?

The man placed a hand on the uniformed woman's shoulder.

Hawwa. I found her in the Tube.

Beneath the layers of foundation, Leila made out pits and scars, the odd mole. Hawwa wore her dye-brown hair bound-up behind her police cap like an extra cerebellum and this, and her air of authority, made her seem taller than she was.

Now wait a minute, Aban. You were wandering, lost, down there in the darkness, and I pulled you up into the light.

Halleluiah!! Praised be the Lord! Strike up the organ!

Everything he says has two meanings, Leila informed Hawwa.

I know the type. Snake-tongues.

Yazid interjected.

These cards were hewn from the Silver Tree.

The Silver Tree? Hawwa seemed startled. Leila could see the wrinkles now.

Yazid pinched Hawwa's cheek.

Oww!! How dare you!

He began to light another cigar.

And you, Aban, you just stand there like a weak old man!

Aban did not look like a weak old man. He was as tall as Yazid, though of bulkier build. The lower part of his face was silvery-grey. Yazid rested his cigar on the edge of the ash-tray, unbuttoned his jacket and began to shuffle the cards.

Ah! We like our little games, don't we, Leila.

Leila ignored him. Aban swigged at the booze. Yazid waved his cards at Aban.

I see you, screwing slowly with the trains rolling past and the beatific, matriarchal ghosts of WACCI and WAAF looking on. Hot jazz, big trombones. We'll meet again…Every action has its consequence, down through the generations.

Leila broke in, quietly.

Sorry we disturbed you, Aban.

You are the intruder! snapped Hawwa. What were you doing here?

Leila sprang up and shoved the policewoman aside.

None of your business!

Don't you lay your filthy paws on me!

Yazid came between them.

Subway swingers, eh? He winked.

Hawwa began to pace around the chamber.

We need only the strong-hearted, the long-boned. Iron and steel and firm, thin lips.

Aban stared at the floor. She was unstoppable.

The story of our civilisation is basically that of continuous progress, with perhaps… one or two hiccoughs.

As her speech progressed, Yazid mimed as though he was being shot several times in the chest, but she seemed not to notice.

We were simply better at everything. The world as we know it would not be as we know it if we had not known more than they knew.

Yazid whispered into Leila's ear,

The Armada is coming!! Ah, Leila, looks like we're in it together.

Leila shifted away from him. Aban sighed and looked searchingly at Yazid.

We just wanted space, privacy, silence. These hands drew concrete from the earth. We pulled the strings of rational magic and made the snake of fate dance upon its tail. Every pebble was symbolic of the whole. Our anchor, Heisenberg's many brains, his uncertainty, our guiding principle. Through pure ideas, we fashioned homes, offices, factories, forges and our song was the song of the blacksmith.

Hands-on-hips, Leila guffawed.

So it was you who put up all this crap!

Yes, well, I am an architect. Bridges are my specialty, and skyscrapers — bridges to the sky, you might say. It didn't quite work out the way I'd planned. Costs, concepts and people had to be…rationalised.

He brightened up.

But the parks are the redeeming feature. I personally picked seeds from the banks of the three original rivers: Tigris, Euphrates and Styx. I planted the first spade into the hard, biochemical earth.

Leila swung her arms and whirled balletically around the chamber.

I love parks, the breeze on my skin, the sunlight flickering through the leaves.

She stopped beneath the gaze of the WAAF officer, shuddered, and drew her arms around her body.

But here, I feel as though I am in a coffin.

We could sit down, have a drink and I could explain it to you, Aban offered.

Glaring at Leila, Hawwa looped arms with Aban.

Sorry, love. He's busy.

I was just offering the girl a drink.

Leila went around to Aban's other side and she, too entangled herself triumphantly.

Yes, thank you. I would like that. Let's go for a tipple and you can tell me all about the castles, the monorails and the bridges.

Yazid drew in the air with his cigar.

They lead from nowhere to nowhere.

Leila and Aban began to dance a slow waltz. Yazid followed them around, playing an imaginary violin He whispered to Hawwa,

She's quite gone, poor dear. Too many loose screws.

Hawwa folded her arms, knitted her brows.

Not a bad dancer, though.

Leila was racing.

I could come to love it here! Imagine the two of us, trapped for ever and ever. No past, no future. Just the moment.

I thought you didn't like darkness, whispered Aban.

Love 'n' hate: a hair's breadth.

They all stopped dead, but the dancers' fingers remained entwined.

Don't imagine too much, Leila, Aban said.

Leila disengaged and began to pace around him.

Do you not desire to lose yourself in the unmapped conduits beneath the city you built? The deeper you go, the more you know. That evening, I was dancing through a fluttering pergola of leaves…

Hawwa moved to stand in her way.

Are police officers, the reluctant guardians of this Silver Age, to be denied even the possibility of love? Aban and I wished to partake of a moment's privacy, away from the cameras and the iris scans and the plastic hoardings, to be awake yet unwatched. We traced our way through manholes and barbed wire and along varnished bricks until we could no longer hear the crowds and somehow, we ended up here. There was a way in, so there must be a way out. I have it in my head…somewhere.

Yazid clicked his heels together and rendered an exaggerated salute.

Ah! The dark blue surge through your veins, the bobbed hair, the body armour, the row of bright, silver buttons, waiting to be unplucked…

He put his finger to his lips.

You have the right to remain silent…
Hawwa continued.

This was not what millions down the ages gave their lives for. Our sacred hearts' blood, flowing down dark channels into the silver stream, our dreams, lucid bullets, fired through the Empyrean.

Yazid raised his arms like a conductor. He sniffed the air, twice.

I feel an epic coming on. Raise a symphony of the nation!

Yazid began to conduct maniacally. A distant rumbling sound came from above. His music ended suddenly, leaving him contorted. Wrists crossed over at his back, he shuffled towards Hawwa.

O Great Woman-in-Blue, harbinger of Peace and Salvation, please, for the sake of Truth, Beauty and the Nation, loop your iron hoops around this poor flesh! Frisk me and take me down, down, into your cold darkness.

The rumbling sound grew louder. Everything began to shake and tremble. The lantern-light flickered on and off. Hawwa went into official mode.

Do not be alarmed. It is merely the trains, running on time.

It is my life, coming after me, Leila whispered.

You're not so important, love. I see your type, day in, day out, dead and blue in the gutters.

Leila went up close to her face and spat out her words.

Fascist cow!

Yazid clapped in camp fashion.

Ah! So city and yet also sturdily demotic, almost bucolic! Fascist cow! The night dance begins!

How about that drink, Leila? Aban persisted.

Oh no, Yazid broke in. You cannot depart so soon, father. First, we must play our game. He began to shuffle the pack.

I don't play cards.

Suddenly, Leila was a coquette.

Why not, Aban? I think it might be fun.

Yazid splayed the deck face-down before her. Girlishly, she picked a card and held it close to her chest. Aban and Hawwa followed suit, guardedly and they sat cross-legged in a circle on the floor. Yazid closed his eyes.

In the Beginning, there was darkness, and God moved upon the face of the waters.

Leila spoke insistently.

In the beginning, I was running through the woods.

Hawwa was cynical.

And someone was following you, right?

The wood was filled with singing, said Leila.

A thousand choirs, said Yazid.

Aban pointed at the door.

I've had enough of this.

He looked at Leila.

Coming?

Aban got up and walked to the door. The handle did not budge.

Yazid opened his eyes.

What did you see in him, Hawwa?

There was another earth-tremor and the four of them jumped up and were flung around the chamber. The cards scattered and Leila began to sob.

We're all going to die!

Yazid laughed.

Yes. It is the truth. Someday, we shall all be dust, blown off a counterpane by the breath of a fly. Bzzzzzzzz!!!!!

Her voice trembled.

Do you know the way out of here, Constable?

Yazid interrupted.

Amongst the rubble and bone of the catacombs, she will plant incriminating evidence, raise false flags. Relax and enjoy your new-found privacy. The here-and-now is all there is.

But Hawwa wasn't buying it.

You've been very wordy about the rest of us, yet we know nothing about you.

Yasin poked Hawwa in the ribs several times as he talked.

We put you in your place that you might maintain us in ours.

Shuffling the cards, he walked away.

I can spot a liar one light year away, maybe two.

Yazid spun around.

Ah, so you're not one of those neurotic detectives who wear beige raincoats and spend all night shadowing the rubber wheel, drinking espresso doppio and monitoring infidelitrous liaisons.

Reality is shifts. Reality is forms, filled rolls and inauthentic fish 'n' chips. Reality is a marble slab and six feet of earth.

Yazid went up close to Hawwa and began to tinker with the buttons on her jacket.

Reality is nine-tenths of fantasy. Or is it the other way around? One minute, the city is around you, above you; buses, monorails, microwave radiation, all the cons of modernity; and the next…

He clicked his fingers up close to her face, startling her.

…Gone! And you're back a hundred years, or a thousand, and everything smells of jasmine, rose, lotus. Bones.

Yazid half-closed his eyes and moved away. He took off his jacket, rolled up his shirt and began to perform a belly-dance around them, touching the posters as he went and quietly singing, Habibi Ya Habibi!

Leila broke in.

I saw it, in a dream. A building suspended, ninety-nine floors, by a fast-flowing river. Thirty thousand tonnes of steel, twisted, reinforced, impregnable, resistant to a Force Twelve Gale. In an earthquake, it swings. And growing beside it, a great, silver tree. Two people on the blade of the ledge, poised on the wire, silent like angels.

Hawwa became distressed and ran up to Leila and held her by the arms.

No! Stop! Please!

But she went on.

A million years ago, this chamber was the surface and there were no people, no dreams, just trees, beasts and mud. Sunlight through a dragonfly's wing. And so it will be, again.

She cupped her ear.

Can you not hear it, the bullock-cart that clatters backwards through time? The layers of the city, laid like dead lovers, one upon the next? As the buildings and bridges collapse and fold like playing-cards, as the

Great Black Friend rises above the rim of His horizon, it is the last thing we shall know.

Aban began to gather up the cards.

Look, he said, they're all aces. The whole pack, aces. No-one can win.

The strange chanting began again. Yazid held the lantern up before his face.

A circlet of stars! A quickening flame.

He was whispering.

Breath, wind...

He blew out the flame.

Darkness.

The disordered chant was silenced by a long, human howl. Hawwa stepped forwards and began to address an imaginary crowd.

It grew right there, in the park in the middle of the city. Its trunk was barely thirty centimetres across and yet it grew hundreds of metres into the air so that its topmost branches were level with the tallest of the buildings. The Silver Tree was an impossibility in a rational landscape. It mocked our city, our civilisation, which was the most advanced in the history of the world. As it grew it reminded us of our mortality, our limitations. All my life had been about the focusing of the will. In search of perfection, the architect had fused the human with the inhuman — but along with the wondrous buildings, there came this infernal tree! And no-one seemed to bother! But I saw it, every day I saw it. And I knew that it would have to be destroyed. And so, one dark night, beneath a low, bitten moon, I took a saw and a spade and, there, in full dress uniform, I climbed over the high walls and dropped down into the park. The trunk was tough, green and alive, it tore the skin of my hands, but I was determined. I watched the tree as it teetered and then fell into the water. I rubbed the dirt, sap and blood off my hands and went down to the rail by the slowest, deepest part of the river, and gazed down into the darkness for what seemed like hours.

Hawwa pulled her hands into a gun-shape and spun around in an arc.

And that's when I saw it. The head, floating in the water. Now, I've seen all kinds of stuff. But there are limits. And when the eyes turned around in their sockets and fixed their gaze on me and when the mouth opened and began to speak, that was somewhat beyond my limit.

After that, the Head appeared in all the stations of my life. Every time I tried to fall asleep, it would whisper in my ear. And always, it would be smiling as though at some private joke. They say that a city is like a tree — the roots go down as far as the branches go up. Aban pretends to logic and rationality, but he and the city he built are seamed through with weakness, compromise and ugliness. Without us police, it would all fall apart. Yet I was in love with the failed architect, with the man and with his buildings. And with one building in particular. Ninety-nine storeys high, by the river, by the Silver Tree.

That night, I climbed the ninety-nine floors of Aban's skyscraper. I was searching for the architect. And still, the head yabbered on and on, even unto the edge of the dawn. From the ninety-ninth floor, I watched the light break over the world's rim. I felt the cool breeze rise from the river and envelope me like a silver hand.

She began to pace around the chamber in ever-decreasing circles.

Even in the darkness of the deepest pit, there is always a sliver of light.

She stopped, and from the holster at her hip removed a gleaming, silver revolver. She caressed the gun and then spun the barrel.

Leila was running a silent film on a battered metal projector. Aban entered the chamber. She stood up. They embraced and kissed several times, ungainly at first.

Why do you watch these?

She shook her head.

I can't remember...

Aban put his arm around her.

It doesn't matter.

Leila took both his hands in her's.

In these dark, echoing crypts, we fell in love.

His lips tasted salty, but were warm. Like his heart, she thought and then she dismissed the sentiment. She pointed upwards.

Listen, Aban! Do you not hear it? Did

you not hear it as you modelled the city on the chambers of your mind?

Aban shook his head.

A river, flowing into concrete and glass. Humanity becoming the world. The world, becoming human. Underneath, the city is seamed through with these dark tunnels, these possible stations. As the icebergs melt and the surface of the world burns with war and solar radiation, the only refuge is here, in the bosom of the earth, in the clutch of cold stone and old music.

Do you still dream, Leila, of the world above?

As I watch the films, they begin to alter. I no longer know whether I am seeing what was there, or what I would like to see.

Perhaps, now, there is no difference.

Yazid entered the chamber, cradling a large tin.

A veritable parliament of baked beans!

Aban smiled.

That's very useful, Yazid.

Yazid moved closer to Leila.

I really don't know what an attractive woman like you sees in a nuts-and-bolts man.

He fixed Aban with a stare.

I found the plans under your pillow, Aban.

Aban's smile vanished.

Leila looked questioningly from one to the other.

They...they were Hawwa's, Aban began. My idea was for a series of elliptical structures that would subsume the whole of the city, each structure nestling inside the next. Everything was calculated down to the last yocto-metre. It would circulate, it would sweat and discharge, excrete and secrete. And it would dream.

Yazid cut in.

The component parts of which would have to come together at a certain point in time in order not to collapse and destroy the entire city. The domino effect, yes?

It was quite safe.

Safe as eggs 'n' sperm, you mean!

The homeostasis was dependent upon many variables.

Variables, like marbles, tend to roll downhill.

Aban was suddenly passionate.

A totally integrated city-state, animate and inanimate beings united in a loose and ever-changing plexus of existence. It was a vision for the future! For ever.

Utopia, in a brick, Yazid laughed.

He went over to the wall and slapped his palm against the old posters.

You went grey, planning all this. It took the best of you. And the worst.

Leila stared straight up into the cold distance of the wartime heroine.

This place, it heals one, she whispered.

Aban's voice trembled.

I met the policewoman at the city's heart. She rose like an angel in a pillar of silver...

Yazid smiled.

Your memory fails you, sweet geometer.

...directing the flow, from on-high.

A traffic-cop!

I would go there at the same time every day.

High noon.

I watched her lift her arms, turn her body, nod, scowl slightly at the chaos: White face, black eyes, a silent sage. She gave me direction.

Yazid clasped his hands across his chest and sighed. Aban did not seem to notice.

We seemed perfectly matched, our hands like those of waltzers.

Yazid got up, stretched his arms.

A woman, a city, a symphony!

She had knowledge. She had plans.

The plans I found under your pillow.

She told me she had dug them out from the Police Archives.

They were hatched in concrete, many years ago.

Leila glanced from one to the other.

What plans, Aban?

Aban's eyes were streaked with red.

Thousands of directives, in search of the perfect State.

Yazid held up a thick bundle of papers.

Full of Castilian colons.

Give me that!

Aban tried to snatch the bundle from him but Yazid forced him down and back against the edge of the table. His thumbs met around Aban's windpipe.

No, Yazid!

Leila screamed and grabbed Yazid's arms.

But he threw her off and tightened his grip. Aban gurgled and his head fell back.

You wrote the language of the city, but each word held within it the seed of its own destruction.

Aban managed for a moment to free himself.

I built bridges, not chains!

At the centre of all truths there is a great lie. In a fundamentally unequal society, it is not possible to conceive of real harmony. Therefore the harmony must be enforced.

Leila launched herself at Yazid, but he cast her down easily and leapt onto Aban's back. Hawwa entered the chamber.

Let him go!!

Her hair had turned silver and streamed like a waterfall over her shoulders. Her cap had gone. She aimed her pistol straight at Yazid and spoke slowly.

Let him go now, or I will shoot you.

Yazid laughed.

Has your brain gone for a walk? There is no holding things down any more. The coordinates that once were fixed have all begun to dance. Chaos rules! Creative destruction. Constant war. And so we witness the birth-pangs of a new Cosmic Order!

Hawwa fired, once. But Leila had rushed into her and the bullet smashed into the ceiling. Hawwa swung at her and Leila fell to the floor and was still. Dust and rubble came down onto Yazid's head. Aban sprang free and began to nurse his neck. His voice was grit.

Put down the gun, Hawwa.

Hawwa pointed the gun first at Yazid and then at Leila. She shook her head, slowly.

So you can stay here, with your little whore?

Leila struggled to her feet and began to limp around the chamber. Blood matted her hair and trickled down the left side of her face and her eyes were glazed over.

It was a sunlit evening. I was strolling through the garden of the city. I was dreaming of another place. Of larks, and emptiness. In the distance, the undulating forms of the hills, the ringing of church bells. Then a breeze got up. The leaves began to dance crazy dances. Cold, cold, cold.

She drew her arms around her.

Running now, running from the city, from its past, its present. I loved her. I thought I knew every beat, every pulse of her body, her soul. I thought we would dance together, through the night.

Hawwa broke in.

A light in the sky made me raise my head from the street-level piss-crap. There, on the ninety-ninth floor, I saw the mason.

Aban's voice spirit-levelled.

I had taken up residence on the top floor of the unfinished building. Every morning, I would await dawn's beauty: the river, curling like a vine towards the far horizon, giving off tributaries like roots. It's amazing how little food one requires, up there, in the sky.

Leila was breathless.

I was moving down a tunnel of darkness. The leaves were pressing in.

Aban circled the table.

For years, I had gazed at the Silver Tree, I had watched it grow. I had gazed for so long, the backs of my eyes had burned with its light. And I dreamed of building a city in the image of the tree. A city of impossible elegance. Yet even as I forged the polis upon an anvil of iron, bar by bar I felt run beneath my fingers like sap beneath bark, some essence that I could never wholly know. The bridges we built have led only to fields of battle.

Hawwa was like a djinn. Her voice was fire.

The only silver is in the pips on my shoulders and the metal of my gun.

Smoke from Yazid's cigar seemed to fill the chamber.

So, architecto, this morning, as the sun rises, you want to throw yourself off the ninety-ninth floor of your tallest skyscraper. You are an angel, flying through the sunlight. The world runs before you, around you, inside you, then contracts to zero.

On the ledge, I felt a movement at my back.

I was an office-worker, high in a tower, the great human resource.

Leila swigged twice from the bottle of booze, then threw it at the wall, where it smashed and tore the WAAF poster, the cream complexion suddenly bleeding port wine from its left eye.

Redemption was a burger and a smiling, Californian actor, blown to five times human size. That morning, I saw something move in the building opposite. I went over to the windows. The windows that can never be opened.

And you saw her arrive. Aban's lover of ninety nights.

Leila held Aban's head between her hands and pulled him close. Her fingers streaked blood onto his cheeks.

I was there as your dreams began to dance. You turned the dead shopping-malls into living, breathing spaces, you ploughed swords into the swelling concrete and drew them up as orchards, waterwheels and joyous maqamat. You wished to turn the city into a musical composition with no beginning and no end, a city that would run through time and space and spirit. For centuries, we have been rising, you and I. I was there with you in the deep, dark dungeons of the Grand Duchy, I danced in the socialist sunset as the piano faded into the silence of the Bomb and I was there as the great dreams of capital foundered and broke apart on the silver altar of war. And I was watching you, that day as you wavered on the ninety-ninth floor, the breeze blowing your hair backwards as though it was the breath of your long-dead mother. Perhaps it was my gaze that drew you to this. We had never met, yet I felt as though I had known you always. I, too was broken as she snapped the trunk of the tree. My blood flowed, silver and red, into the earth and down, into the river. Perhaps, eventually, to the sea.

Hawwa's voice ballooned with panic.

The electricity of my thoughts was disturbed. Something possessed my soul!

Leila turned to her. Spoke quietly.

When you broke the Tree, you released Yazid.

The policewoman gazed tearfully at Leila and then at her own palms. She was almost whispering.

My hands were bleeding sap. I'm...I'm sorry.

Yazid smiled.

Ah! Blame it on the vegetation. Burning bushes, witches' brushes, bad-hat hawthorn tree. Governor, polizei, subway humper, torturer, Executioner, Holy See. You forget that all the while, through darkening centuries, you were working only for me.

Leila fell against the poster. She was clutching the side of her head as blood dripped through her fingers onto the floor.

I remember now. Before the tunnel, there was the tree. I was naked in the night air and I was gazing into the fast-flowing river, when...

Hawwa's eyes gleamed with tears.

I once saw a man fall from a great height. His face was perfect.

...a dark shadow, behind me, moving ever closer. I am shivering.

Yazid moved towards Leila.

It was fun. Chasing the night dancer down into the belly of the earth.

Heavy breath, upon my neck. That scent...

They say that a hanging woman smells hyacinths.

The air is still. There is only the rushing of the water. By the stump of the Silver Tree, I catch my breath. I grow sleepy.

If the djinns don't get you, the CO_2 will.

A man's hands upon my neck!

Yazid placed his hands lightly around her neck. Rolled his thumbs in their sockets. His voice was almost seductive.

The spirit of the city, between my palms.

My breath, seeping away like mist off water. Everything is darkening, fast.

He lifted his hands away.

Yazid, murderer by occupation, torturer by inclination. Card shark, stock trader, general animal. Grain by grain, I snort my way to heaven.

You killed her? Hawwa was aghast.

Death is quantum. Besides, my dear copper, you are one to talk. Pushed your silver-headed lover off a window-ledge, ninety-nine floors up?

I did not push him! He...he jumped!

But he changed his mind, and stretched out his arm. At that moment, he needed you, Madame Polizei.

I tried to save him! I tried…

Quelle musique!

Aban shook his head.

It's us. We did it.

The gun shook in Hawwa's hands.

If…if I kill him now, perhaps everything will return to normal. We will all go back to the way we used to be. This was just a period of madness. Such things are necessary for a society, from time-to-time.

No, Hawwa, said Aban. All roads lead to the ninety-ninth floor.

Leila wiped the blood out of her eyes. Yazid was grinning from ear-to-ear.

After three thousand years, the djinns will run free!

Aban stood in front of her.

There is no light, no silver, no knowledge. It's all just shuffling cards.

Hawwa handed her gun to Leila.

In the chamber of this revolver, there lies a single, silver bullet, distilled from the innermost sap of the first Silver Tree.

Yazid seemed almost gleeful.

Little people! There is no 'Outside'. There is no 'Surface', no light, no day. No future. There is only Now — and that passes before we know it. The whole world is built on a battlefield. One way or another, everyone makes bullets, swords, bombs, fire. The cities, the financial centres, the governments…in essence, all are about nothing but war. Yet soon, we will be coming to an end. History will end and through the purity of power will we attain a glorious rapture!

Leila ran her finger over the contours of the metal.

Yet I would not exchange it for anything. The living city, with all her contradictions, her wet underbelly, the dark chambers of her heart. Through storms, she trundles on…

Yazid stepped out in front of Leila and assumed the crucifixion position.

Go on then, my love, give me the silver!

Hawwa urged her on.

This way, we will cross the bridge between memory and delusion. Through this one act, the world will become whole again.

But Aban intervened.

You cannot change history with a silver bullet.

Leila looked up at the WACCI woman on the wall.

The power of any building lies in its emptiness. The strength of any society lies in that which remains unthought.

Give it to him now!! Hawwa shouted.

Yazid gazed straight into Leila's eyes. He stretched out his right hand, pulled on the barrel, allowed his lips to fall open just enough to permit its narrow bore to enter, reached down with his left hand and pulled the trigger.

Darkness and heat descend upon everything. When the light from the storm-lantern again becomes visible, the wartime posters and the Dutch master have vanished. On the back wall of the chamber, I am painting the skyline of a postmodern city in red, but the skyline is also teeth, eyes, brain, guts; it is the city as living being. In the distance, there is a tree, a peasant, perhaps some light in the sky. The buildings, cars, birds, trees are intact and society has resumed its quest for perfection. But the Silver Tree has gone — or perhaps it is just that we can no longer see it. We cannot rid ourselves of the past and its dualities, we cannot forget what we are, and yet perhaps through them, like dogs, horses and birds shall we sniff and crow our way to a facsimile of heaven.

Hawwa enters the chamber and rests her hand on my shoulder. Then Aban comes in, holding a scroll. We are the little people and these are the threads that bind us to one another. This is the spirit of the city. Beneath the sun, we do not see the circle of light in the sky. Aban unfurls the scroll on the table and in the guttering light of the storm-lantern, we begin to pore over it.

Silently, from the shadows, you enter. For a while, you stand aside, watching us. Then you take the silver-backed cards from your inside jacket pocket, you shuffle the deck and smile broadly, that old, old smile of yours and you splay the cards out towards me. Now at last I remember the ancient dance, the scent of burning rocks. For I am Leila, Lilith, I am the root, the source, the One who draws the world in her own blood. And however many times you steal away my life, my city, my dreams, like the spinning lights of the universe my dance will never end.

Suhayl Saadi is author of Psychoraag *(Black and White Publishing, 2004) and* The Burning Mirror *(Polygon, 2001). Psychoraag was shortlisted for the 2004 James Tait Black Memorial Prize (for fiction), and the 2005 Patras Bokhari Prize, longlisted for the 2006 International IMPAC Dublin Literary Award and winner of a PEN Oakland Josephine Miles Literature Award. 'The Icarus Tree' was written in response to a Glasgow 2020 event, which brought together young leaders from the Nordic countries with a variety of people from Glasgow.*

†

ZEDTEE

— Les Wood

There was going to be a burning.

It was a pleasure to burn. McGlashan just loved to watch the smoke billow from the piles of flaming furniture on the front grass of some hard case or other. It was the part he liked best. Actually, when he stopped to analyse it, it wasn't the burning itself that gave the most satisfaction (though that was gratifying enough), but the look on the family's faces as they stood in the garden, aghast that such a thing could be happening to them. The streaming tears of the women, the clenched jaws of the men, the wide-eyed wonder of the weans, all of them captivated by the flaring, thundering blaze that was their worldly possessions. And, best of all, it was no use them calling the police. No use at all.

McGlashan was the police.

Part of the ZedTee Team.

McGlashan particularly loved the pleading of the women — Don't dae it son! It's aw we've goat, we've nuthin left! And the men, standing in silent fury, ready to jump in, burst some heads. They were good for a laugh too.

But they were powerless. They knew if they lifted so much as a finger to try to stop them, McGlashan would have a violation order slapped on them and things would get much worse — a wee adjustment to the old identity card and employment rights were revoked, benefits halted. No job, no dole, no life. It was all McGlashan could do to keep himself from laughing in their faces.

That would be unprofessional.

Not the way the ZedTee Team went about their business.

The Team had been together five years now — part of the Crime and Law Revolution of 2015. Unthinkable in pre-Independence Scotland, the reforms put forward by Provost Fraser were instrumental in establishing Glasgow as Scotland's, and indeed the UK's, first Zero Tolerance city. ZedTeeCitee. Not for Glasgow the flimsy strategies and half-hearted posturing of other towns. No siree, for Glasgow it was the full-on, in-your-face, all-or-nothing approach. Zero Tolerance meant exactly that — no crime would be forgiven, no opportunity for remorse or acts of contrition. Zero Tolerance, nothing less. And it was up to officers like McGlashan to make sure the law was upheld.

It was simple really. A sliding scale of punishment to fit the crime, no judge, no jury, no sentence in the Bar-L. All that was required was some fragment of evidence, a photograph, say, or a fingerprint, an eyewitness account, CCTV footage, anything which linked the perpetrator to the crime, and the ZedTee Team moved in. Spray graffiti on a wall? The ZedTees were at your house the next day panning your windows in. Breaking and entering? McGlashan and his crew would be round smashing up your telly, your hi-fi, your computer console. And it was no use pleading poverty, that the telly wasn't paid up yet, or how were you expected to afford a glazier? Too bad. Should have thought of that before you let your boy out on the randan, shouldn't you?

It worked.

Within eighteen months of starting, Zero Tolerance had sent crime levels plummeting. People were forced to face up to the consequences of their actions. Back in the early noughties, the Executive had tried to deal with the problem using ASBOs, curfews, dispersal orders. They were less than useless. Not only did they let the neds get away with it, but they became a badge of honour, a twisted measure of how hard you were — Don't come near me, ya muppet, Ah've goat an ASBO an Ah'm no feart tae yase it! And crime kept getting worse.

They did it because they could get away with it, pure and simple; there were no real penalties. But with Zero Tolerance it soon hit home. You do something bad, something bad gets done to you. See how that feels, eh son? We don't need a stinking ASBO, now we just send in the ZedTee Team to even up the score, eye for an eye, quid pro quo and all that stuff. And you can stop your snivelling —what's your problem pal? If you hadn't done it to someone else, this wouldn't be happening to you, would it? Don't like it? Tough.

Of course, the usual suspects, the Church, the papers and the liberal lefties, all started bleating about the erosion of civil liberties and the rights of the individual to a fair trial and all that justice-for-all guff. But they failed to point out it wasn't their houses in the leafy suburbs that were being wrecked, or their cars left with smashed windscreens on the whim of some evil wee turd tanked up on tonic wine. No, the extent of their problems maybe stretched to having to drive too close to a dodgy scheme on the way home from the office. The truth of the matter was they didn't have a leg to stand on. As soon as the beleaguered, decent folk in the high rises and tenements saw some good old-fashioned revenge and retribution being meted out to the wannabe hard-men, the drug-dealers and the neds whose idea of a good night out was to throw a kitten on a bonfire, the idea was sold. No protest, no problem. Deprivation, poverty were no excuses. Plenty of people lived in terrible circumstances but didn't resort to violence and mayhem. Sure, it was tough if you were brought up in an abusive home, no money, no prospects. It was hard, no doubt about it. But that didn't give you the right to go out and mug a pensioner for a couple of quid. It was a baseball bat in the balls for you, my friend. Maybe next time you'll think twice.

The public loved it. Guys like McGlashan became heroes, the saviour of the schemes, the liberator from fear. McGlashan felt like the Terminator. Every time he pulled on the black and red ZedTee uniform and clambered into the patrol car (the Tit-for-Tat-Mobile, he called it) he felt the rush of adrenaline surge through his arteries, quickening his heart, dilating his pupils. The black gloves were his own idea, not an official part of the uniform, but wearing them pandered to his sense of absolute power and control. The boss had vetoed the shades though. McGlashan was disappointed. They would have completed the picture. For McGlashan it was all part of the symbolism — the uniform, the destruction, the humiliation, they were designed to make sure people never forgot what was happening to them when the ZedTee Team called round.

Not everyone saw it that way though. Some of the new members of the Team were a bit wet behind the ears, thought the Team should be showing a wee bit more social concern for the people who were on the receiving end of that old biblical justice the Team were so expert at. A wee bit of empathy wouldn't go amiss. That would be bloody right. Too much education, that was their problem. Newbie fast-track graduate types wanting a taste of the tough stuff before they moved up in the world. They knew nothing. Empathy. Social concern. That way led straight back to the bad old days. Christ, there was still enough of it going on, despite the best efforts of the ZedTees. McGlashan and the rest of the boys would never let that backward slide happen. No siree.

And today there was going to be a burning. McGlashan sat in the back of the van and allowed a smile to sneak onto his lips. A burning. Oh, yes. He could feel an almost sexual excitement at the prospect. While the Team dealt with other crimes and misdemeanours with what might be termed an honest, if severe, punishment, burning was reserved for the worst of the non-custodial crimes — the serious assaults, the bottlings, the ram-raiding. Then it was the full Team battering down the door unannounced, dragging the contents of the house into the front garden, making a nice big pile, ready to be soused in petrol. Sometimes, if McGlashan was in the right frame of mind, he would make whoever in the family was responsible for bringing all this misery down on their heads light the match, start the fire. He considered it a classy touch. Of course, classy or not, it was often too provocative for the family and a fight might start, some pathetic attempt to get stuck into the Team. But they were always mob-handed enough to take care of that, plenty of police back-up.

It was great fun.

Today it was a drug-dealer. Or rather, a drug-dealer's granny. The wee piece of slime had done a runner. But the Team knew where he'd been holed up, from where he'd been selling the gear. His granny's. What a joke.

Still, it would have to do.

As soon as they pulled into the street, eight of them in the van, two police cars full of heavies as support, McGlashan knew something would kick off. Something with

the newbies. It was a poor area, the houses mostly FlatPaks, cheap and flimsy, but still too good for the likes of the low-life that lived around here. They didn't know how lucky they were, most of them — council housing like this didn't come cheap to law-abiding taxpayers like McGlashan. But there were two lily-livered, greenhorn saps on the Team today, and this was just the sort of place and situation to get one of them fired up about social injustice and inequalities and the like. McGlashan could see it in their eyes.

The van drew up outside the house. McGlashan scanned the Team. 'Right, boys,' he said. 'Let's make this a fast one. In. Out. Do the deed. No faffing around.' He flexed his fingers inside his gloves, the creaking of the leather sending a shiver along his spine.

They piled out, McGlashan ushering them up the stairs towards the front door. 'Wait a minute,' he said. He tried the handle. It turned easily and the door swung open. He grinned. 'Excellent,' he said. 'No need for the old battering ram.'

They ran into the house, shouting for everyone to stay calm, it was the ZedTees. McGlashan found the old woman in the kitchen, her arms immersed to the elbows in the suds in the sink. She stood, white-faced and blinking uncomprehendingly, mouthing soundless words. He walked over and put his arm around her shoulder. She offered no resistance as he guided her out to the garden, all the while taking his time to explain what was happening and why. Her slippers slapped on the concrete like grounded fish as he led her down the steps. The others dragged the sofas, the tables, sideboards onto the front grass. Someone heaved the television through the front window. The old woman gave a startled jump. McGlashan could tell she didn't have a clue what was going on. He could feel her shaking, saw her chin quivering. He felt his own breathing becoming, deeper, more intense. This was what made it all worthwhile.

A few neighbours had gathered in the street. They shouted and screamed at the Team to stop, she was just an old woman, she'd never done anyone any harm. The police, riot sticks pulled and extended, held them back. McGlashan allowed himself a small smile. He took out the Zero Tolerance order, handed it to the woman. She took it from him with trembling fingers, looked at him with a mixture of puzzlement and despair. McGlashan took her a little to the side. 'You know the real reason this is being done don't you?' he whispered in her ear.

'Naw, son. I don't,' she replied, her eyes filling with tears.

'The real reason,' he continued whispering, 'is that we, my Team, can get away with it. No-one can stop us.' He paused, gazed into the distance. 'No-one.'

'I don't even know who yous are,' she said, her voice breaking.

McGlashan looked at her. 'I just told you who we are. I've served you the order. This is your punishment.'

'Punishment for what?'

'For letting that wee toerag of a grandson of yours sell all sorts of crap from your front door.'

'But that was him,' she said. 'It wisnae me.' She frowned. 'What was it?'

He stared at her. 'What?'

'What was it he was selling?'

He laughed. 'Don't act like you don't know. I've seen your type before. Sweetness and light. Butter wouldn't melt, and all that crap.'

'But I don't,' she said.

He looked beyond her shoulder towards the bonfire. It was a pitifully small pyre. One of the guys had the jerry cans out, pouring the petrol over the furniture. He winked at her. 'Too late for that now, hen,' he said. 'It's burning time.'

McGlashan marched over to join the others as the old woman glanced at the order in her hand, her brow furrowed, seeming to realise for the first time what was about to happen. 'Wait!' she called.

He ignored her, carried on walking. He reached into his pocket and brought out his matches.

'This isn't right,' he heard someone say. McGlashan looked up, expecting to see one of the johhny-come-latelies, lipping off. He was wrong. It was Carlin, one of the regular guys. One of the original Team from back in '15.

'What's your problem?' McGlashan asked.

'This whole set-up,' said Carlin. 'Look at her. She doesn't have a clue. This has got nothing to do with her. We shouldn't be punishing her. She's not to blame.'

'Of course she's to blame,' said McGlashan. 'She knew. You mean to tell me there were all these weirdos coming round the door at all hours of the day and night and she didn't put two and two together? She thought her grandson was just this really popular guy, loads of pals wanting to visit whenever they liked?' He shook his head. 'Nah, that doesn't wash with me.'

'It's still not her fault.' This time it was Docherty, another one of the old guard.

What the hell was going on? Had those little bleeding-hearts newcomers been getting to them? Trying to subvert the course of justice? He spotted the both of them skulking beside the van. Skulking! They'd been up to something. McGlashan jerked his thumb towards them. 'Don't let those softies put you off.' The men turned to see who he was meaning. 'They're just a pair of ignorant fools. They don't realise what this job is all about. They don't see its importance to law and order.'

'What are you talking about?' said Carlin. 'They haven't said a word to us. This is nothing to do with them. The rest of us,' he indicated the other ZedTee members, 'we've been discussing this old dear.'

'Aye,' said Docherty. 'It's the boy, not her, we should be going after.'

'You know the rules,' said McGlashan angrily. This was turning out all wrong. 'A burning is to be done at the last known residence of the perpetrator. That's what the legislation says.'

'Screw the legislation.' Baxter this time. This was becoming a full-blown mutiny. 'We're dealing with a human being here, not some words in a lawyer's textbook.'

McGlashan snorted. 'We deal with human beings every day, guys. This isn't any different.'

'Aye it is,' said Docherty. 'She's innocent. Does she look like a drug-dealer to you?'

'That's beside the point,' said McGlashan. 'It clearly states that…'

'We've decided,' Carlin interrupted.

McGlashan stared at him. 'Decided what?'

'We're having nothing to do with this,' Carlin said. He glanced around him, took in the rest of the Team. 'All of us. We can't do it. Not this time.' The rest of the men stood, stonily silent, arms folded.

McGlashan laughed. 'What do you mean? Christ, take a look at yourselves, you sorry bunch of morons. Not five minutes ago you were splashing fuel all over her best furniture. It's ruined now anyway.' Out of the corner of his eye he saw the old woman making her way back up the stairs, entering the house, the Zero Tolerance order clutched in her hand. 'Look at her,' he said. 'She's resigned to it. She knows there's nothing she can do.'

'Maybe so,' said Baxter. 'But that's just what we can do. Nothing.'

The situation was getting completely out of hand. He had to stamp some authority on the proceedings. He took a match from the box, struck it with a sizzling flare against the sandpaper on the side.

'McGlashan, don't!' shouted Docherty. 'Think what you're doing. This is wrong. You know it.'

McGlashan stood with the match poised above the furniture. The flame flickered and danced on the tip, a bright, comforting glow against the grey sky. He was faintly aware of the yelling from the crowd in the street. The sound seemed to recede to a distant murmur. An irritation, nothing more. The men, too, retreated to the edge of his consciousness. The flame was all. He could feel its heat as it burned its way down the matchstick. It was a pleasure to burn. Oh yes.

The law must be upheld.

Les Wood's 'ZedTee' was a prize winner in the Glasgow 2020 competition for Glasgow University Creative Writing Masters course students.

†

GLASGOW'S PANTS

— Anne Donovan

Folk are always asking how it happened. How did a city with the worst record for everything in the world, turn itsel round in such a short time? How did Glasgow become the hottest tour destination ever?

Let's start at the beginning. Ten year ago, when Edinburgh looked set tae take over the world and Glasgow was appearing bottom of every league table under the sun (except for membership of Gamblers Anonymous) there we were, clocked in the middle of wanny they endless meetings, throwing ideas around. Might as well chuck a ball about for all the good they done.

Ah hated it. After a lifetime in the Parks Department, when they'd finally built over hauf the parks and computerised everything, ah'd been shunted intae some Micky Mouse organisation whose mission statement was improving quality of life for the socially challenged (i.e. neds). Funny, ah thought growing plants and trees was improving the quality of life, but naw, ah was surplus tae requirements, and had tae put up and shut up tae get my enhanced pension. Which meant sitting in a windowless room wi Archie, who'd been sumpn tae dae wi a Heiland Dancing Roadshow, and Shug, a retired plumber who'd run his ain business for years and couldnae staund being idle so he'd got hissel on the Regenerate Glasgow Committee.

We were supposed tae be finding some way tae put Glasgow back on the map, some new slogan or theme that would have everybody and his auntie flocking here. But everything we came up with was a no-no.

Glasgow — Green City?

No since they built hooses on hauf the parks and ran a motorway through what was left.

Glasgow — Clean City?

Graffiti City mibbe.

Or Chuggie City.

Aye you cannae walk doon a street wioot gettin it stuck tae yer shoes. How come folk don't just chuck it in a bin or stick it on their mobile for later?

Let's face it, said Archie, Glasgow's pants.

That's it. Shug's eyes were shining.

What?

Pants.

Aye but you can hardly attract tourists by telling them Glasgow's pants.

Naw, but you can get them tae buy Glasgow's pants. Shug leaned his elbows on the table, looked round us.

Look, it's a waste of time trying tae get folk tae come here by kidding on we're like Edinburgh. Everybody knows it's got a castle, a festival, all that stuff.

Archie bristled. We've got festivals too. Hunners of them — Jazz, Celtic Connections, the River Festival...

Aye but Edinburgh's got it sorted; three weeks during the English school holidays, when all the Scottish scruffbag weans are back at school so they won't annoy anybody.

Archie still looked pissed aff but said nothing.

All the media types fly up fae London in a wanner — for three weeks they review everything in the *Telegraph* and BBC2 and you cannae get a cubbyhole tae stay in for love nor money. Edinburgh folk make a fortune then sit back on their arses for the resty the year while the tourists dauner round the castle and buy Scottie dug brooches and tartan scarfs.

Ah thought ah'd better move things on a bit so ah dug out sumpn I'd been taught in the 'Reflective Skills for Committee Personnel' course last year.

So you don't like Edinburgh, Shug. But perhaps there's something we can learn from them.

It's no a question of liking or no liking. Ah'm just saying it's a waste of time for us tae compete wi them on culture.

We've got culture too.

Look, Archie, it's got nothing tae dae wi culture. Of course we've got just as much culture as them — mair, in fact. Rennie Macintosh, Greek Thomson, no tae mention all the young cutting edge artists — they're all fae Glasgow — d'ye ever hear of anybody famous ever gaun tae Edinburgh Art School? They'd be too busy having afternoon tea and painting geraniums tae dae any real art. And as for thon city of literature crap — maisty the great writers are fae Glasgow.

Walter Scott?

Who reads him nooadays?

Ian Rankin?

Aye, ah'll gie you yer Ian Rankin right enough but name wan mair?

Alexander McCall Smith, Muriel Spark, Robert Louis Stevenson...

He was really fae Glasgow.

Naw he wasnae.

He was — he was a Jekyll and Hyde character.

Ah pitched in wi my quiet chairperson voice. Look folks, ah hate tae be a wet blanket but this is getting us naewhere. Look at the publicity — the headlines are getting worse no better. We've got tae dae something aboot Glasgow's image.

Shug shook his heid. Stuff the image, we're looking at it all wrang.

He poured hissel mair coffee. Edinburgh's all image, right? All show, nae substance.

Archie nodded. Fur coat and nae knickers.

That's it exactly — while Glasgow's pants.

Ah cannae see that as a selling point.

Can you no? Big posters with 'Glasgow's Pants' on them. And a huge photie of a pair of drawers.

Who's gonnae go tae a city that advertises itsel as being pants?

No being pants, making them. Shug nibbled a bourbon cream. The only reason we want tae get tourists tae come here is tae make money out them. Why no just make money by selling something?

Pants?

Everybody needs them.

Unless they come fae Edinburgh.

Glasgow has a solid industrial and manufacturing past.

Aye, shipbuilding.

There's no that much difference between engineering and lingerie manufacture right enough.

Yous are getting bogged doon — let's start simple. A factory churning out novelty pants. Wan basic shape for men, wan for women. Coupla patterns — say 'Let Glasgow Flourish' with the bell, the tree and the fish. And Rennie Macintosh pants, wi the wee rose on it.

Archie smiled. Why not dae Paddy's market pants — get them second hand.

You've got nae vision.

Ah've got nae vision. And you think Glasgow can be regenerated by making novelty pants?

But somehow, Shug had his way. It started small, no the big splash he'd wanted. A grant fae some development corporation or another, free council premises in the east end cause the three machinists working for us would increase the employment rate in the scheme by a hundred and fifty percent. Then a website and some cheap ads during the waterbingo games on TV in the middle of the night.

And it just took aff. Unbelievable. At first it was the Rennie Mac wans that sold then gradually the Glasgow coat of arms went too.

And at another meeting, three months intae the enterprise, we fell on the real goldmine. It was Archie's idea tae dae something about football but as usual it took Shug tae see the way forward.

Celtic and Rangers pants — in a city of footie fans it's a pure banker, says Archie.

Naa, we don't want tae be associated wi Celtic or Rangers.

Why no Partick Thistle?

Shug gied me wanny his looks. Why no Maryhill Juniors? He scratched his ear. We don't want tae dae the conventional footie fan stuff — we want something anti-sectarian, that'll take in baith Rangers and Celtic.

Aye it's good tae dae something wi a vision.

Vision? said Shug. We want something that'll get us another grant, and backing fae baith the big teams. He thumped the table. Got it!

Glasgow City of Harmony boxers had Celtic stripes on the left hauf and Rangers ones on the right. The slogan was 'Lean left, lean right, be in Harmony tonight'.

The first run sold out in a week. Mair and mair folk had tae be employed produc-

ing them and the incredible thing was that they started tae go down big time in Japan — don't ask me why but they couldnae get enough of them.

By then things had grown that much that ah'd been seconded tae the Glasgow's Pants Enterprise full time. Me, Shug and Archie done the business plans, well Shug done them and me and Archie rubberstamped all his ideas. Shug had taken on an assistant, George, Georghe as was, who'd come fae Romania the year afore and set up his ain chain of sandwich shops, Little Pieces of Heaven. And there was Shazia and Arfan, who ran the design and manufacturing side of it. But though we were daeing fine we still only had one factory space with a cubbyhole for Shazia's designs and a wee office for us. Arfan done all his business fae his mobile and was always either jumping about the factory, or on a plane somewhere. He liked tae describe hissel as a 'hands on, bum off manager'.

Then one day, we got a phone call fae some guy in Kyoto saying he had a group of tourist wanted tae come and see the factory. I put the phone on mute and turned tae Shug.

Will I just say we don't dae tours?

Are you aff yer heid? He switched the sound on. Of course we can do a tour of the factory for your clients. Now, do you have the rest of the holiday organised yet? Dramatic pause. Edinburgh? Oh dearie me. No...no, well, I suppose they still could go there, assuming they have had all their vaccinations.

You hadn't heard about the funnel web spider infestation? Edinburgh City Council Tourist Board have been very irresponsible, in my opinion, but of course they don't want any panic. No, it's totally confined to Edinburgh city centre — you see they have all these old drains and pipes under the castle and surrounding area. Glasgow's plumbing is very modern and we can certainly put up your party in a luxury hotel, arrange your sightseeing as well as a tour of the factory. All at a great price.

You had tae hand it tae Shuggie, he was never one tae let truth get in the way of a good business opportunity. So the first ever Glasgow's Pants minibreak was arranged.

And did those folk have a ball! Shug negotiated a good deal at a top hotel on the grounds that this was only the beginning of a huge enterprise, which of course it turned out tae be. In every room, alang with the Campsie mineral water, Caramel Log and Clydeherbs shampoo were complimentary his and hers themed pants, each with a Glasgow landmark on it. At first we had a random selection of buildings printed on them but as we got customer feedback forms and slicked up wur act, the ladies got a Rennie Mac rose and the guys got thongs with the uni tower on them. Very popular. There were sightseeing trips of all the usual places in and around Glasgow and curry nights out, as well as the big highlight, the trip round the factory.

That first time, I couldnae see how we were gonnae make it interesting.

After all, it's just a load of folk working away at sewing machines and the design room's that wee you couldnae have a busload of tourists piled intae it.

You don't think ah'm gonnae let them in the design room, dae ye?

Ah looked blank.

This might be a cover — industrial espionage.

Oh right, never thought of that.

Shug tapped his heid. That's why you're no the managing director. You don't think ahead, anticipate. You just react tae things.

Anyway, that doesnae answer ma question. How are you gonnae keep them amused for two hours?

Well, there's the dauner round the manufacturing area. Then there's the display of all the designs, cuppa tea and time for them tae make a purchase.

And what are they gonnae dae for the other hour and a hauf?

But as usual ah'd underestimated Shug. When he talked about the display ah thought he meant looking at the pants in the display case in the foyer, but he organised a fashion show wi slinky lassies and guys wi six packs modelling the gear. Well that certainly kept the tourists amused — a lot of steamed-up specs in the room by the time they'd finished. We shifted a ton of merchandise afterwards. No as much as nooadays when we have the market sorted

tae a tee, even know which pants tae punt tae different nationalities. Americans love ones wi tartan on them while the Belgians go a bomb on the retro Tennents lager can scanties. Took some negotiating tae get the rights tae the design but it was worth it.

We even have wur ain song. Held a competition for the best wan — all the big bands were lining up tae write and record it for us, but Shug goat fed up wi them.

Too bloody artyfarty by hauf. We need something simple.

So he got a local primary school class tae write the lyrics and persuaded a team of councillors tae record it.

Whatever yer job,
Whatever you wear,
Whatever you do, wherever you go, you need underwear.
And we've got the best,
We've got whit yes want,
Sauve and elegant,
Wear Glasgow's pants.

We end the tours with everybody singing it just afore they go in tae the shop tae get their souvenirs. The karaoke download goes doon really well too.

Ah guess the rest is history. The tourists kept coming, sales went aff the scales. Internet trade accounted for seventy percent of underwear purchases in Britain alone and Glasgow became the export capital of the UK, gaun fae an unemployment blackspot tae full employment. No just manufacturing but designing, marketing and all that. And the folk who were noo working wanted tae spend their dough, so that meant other businesses grew too. The other day, me and Archie and Shug were staunding in the foyer, waiting tae welcome wur ten thousandth tour, wi photographers and journalists clocked round the entrance.

Look at that, said Shug (Sir Shug noo of course) pointing at the display case. The first perra pants we made, wi the Glasgow coat of arms on it. Let Glasgow Flourish. And it has.

Goes tae show, how something that big can grow fae something that wee. A throwaway phrase.

Tell you what but. It's just as well that

first day, Archie didnae turn round and say Glasgow's mince. That could of been a completely different story.

Anne Donovan is author of the novel Buddha Da (2003) and the short story collection Hieroglyphics and Other Stories (2001), both published by Canongate. Buddha Da was shortlisted for the 2003 Orange Prize and the Whitbread First Novel Award, nominated for the Dublin International IMPAC Award and won the Prince Maurice Award in 2004. Her next novel will be published by Canongate in spring 2008. Winner of the 1997 Macallan/Scotland on Sunday short story competition, she has also written for radio. 'Glasgow's Pants' was written in response to a Glasgow 2020 event involving BBC Scotland journalists and staff.

†

SHE WORE BLUE VELVETEEN

— Marie-Anne Mancio

Andy Scott eyes up the concourse from his seat in the Po-Mo Café. You can tell the scuffers, the pooros, by their clothes. Only real saddos buy their gear in IKEA. He calls it the Braehead-brain dead syndrome.

'Rubbish. I got a skirt there today. A bargain,' his mam said. He and his dad spent the evening laughing at her trying to put it together.

'Sure you got the zip in the right place, pet?' his dad teased.

'There are nae zips,' she snapped. 'IKEA don't do zips. They do Stick-a-Tite.'

'That there's going to be one heck of a draft then.'

She scowled at them both. 'I cannae remember the last time you made something that didnae fall apart after a day.'

It's true. All his folks' stuff is like that. A little bit wonky. It embarrasses him. Like his dad's Yorkshire accent. ('Nowt wrong with me, lad. It's you who speaks funny. The nearest you've been to California is sitting on that couch, staring at that screen. But you sound like you was raised there. When I married your mam, it was her Glaswegian accent I fell for. All you teenagers speak American.')

'Anyway, they do nice men's wear too. I'll take you, Andy.'

'No chance.'

His dad sets down his mug of tea. 'Oh, go on, lad. Think of the fun we could have with a suit. Inside pockets!'

And after IKEA, they come here, to Buchanan's, to look at the decent stuff. The stuff they can't afford. His mam says when he was born, you could walk down Buchanan Street in the open air. So you'd get wet, crossing from one shop to another. But then those were the days people carried their own shopping, bags and bags of it. And hardly anywhere was open twenty-four seven.

All his salary goes on clothes, and all his friends' salary goes on clothes. Some smart arse who called himself a 'cultural analyst' labelled them The Retail Generation. 'Labelled being the apt word,' he smiled smugly on some boring news item. Andy's mam pays him to watch the news with her. He knows his dad thinks that's daft ('If he won't watch it, he won't watch it, lass.') but Andy's got the hang of it now. How to zone out and make out like he's watching. Sometimes, she tries to test him on stuff; tries to start a debate. But he never falls for it. Unless it's about clothes. There's his trainer collection. And his vintage T-shirt collection from the early Noughties. You had to be careful with T-shirts. They could go either way. Rock stars are out; disaster warnings in….He checks his phone. Thirteen minutes past. She'll be taking her break soon, sashaying across the shiny floor, her heels click-clacking, echoing through the mall.

Her name's Mischa. She has eyes the colour of bitter chocolate, the dark expensive kind his Nan likes. And her hair is black. Black as a miner's face, his Grandad liked to say. She works in the tennis racquet shop (Ace!) so he bets she has to listen to losers making jokes about balls. It's a pity they don't make her wear the gear. She'd look great in a tiny white gym skirt and a pair of pumps. He knows all the times of the staff breaks. The Po-Mo Corporation makes sure at least three people are in the Po-Mo café at any one time. Workers are 'encouraged' to eat there, which means it's the only place they give you bloody vouchers for. Not that he minds. He can't be arsed walking up a floor to the food court where all the food looks the same. Ever since the McKeith scandal of 2015, there are cream cakes shaped like vegetables, and meat burgers and deep-fried chips are back on the menu. He bites his nails. He's sure she doesn't like him. She's never even nodded at him in passing, like she does with Larsson or Connor or those other oafs in Sporto.

When the new labels come in and he has to barcode socks, Andy fantasises about getting Mischa back to his bedroom. He'll get his parents out the house. Then he'll hide the really bad stuff. Like the painting of the stones and the fake French posters his mam loves, oh and those lime cushions and the chair shaped like a Polo mint that has been in the living room as long as he can remember. In the fantasy, he impresses Mischa with a half-bottle of sparkling red wine, and then she leans back on his bed, the tips of her black hair brushing his pillow. He bites her neck and tickles her navel until she agrees to take off her pants….And they'd be white and lacy and tie up at the sides with little ribbons like the robo-mannequin's in the shop window of All Things Spice. There are cameras that record when you look in that window. Take an iris print, link to your ID card, send you an e-catalogue (targeted marketing, the Po-Mo Corp calls it). But Andy worries sometimes that his name's down on some register of potential perves.

Ten, nine, eight, seven, six….That piped birdsong is getting on his nerves. Dead on one second. She's got her hair in a ponytail today. It swings from side to side as she walks. A clean, black arc. He can intercept her. He jangles his café tokens in his pockets. Tries to figure out her trajectory. It has to look accidental. He'll do it at the counter, when she's swiping her sandwich. He stands. No, now. As she's reaching out, hesitating between the Chinese tofu on rye and the Italian curry on baguette.

'Can I date you some time?' he says, reaching out to touch the sleeve of her black cardigan. He is so nervous he almost doesn't notice it's a nylon mix.

Mischa shrugs, picking up a can of non-fizz Cola. She flicks a token onto the counter. Say something. Say no, then. Say anything…

Then she walks off.

He sprints after her. What am I doing? Am I crazy? 'Hey! Hey, wait up? That a yes?'

'Depends.'

'On what?'

She stares at him, weighing him up. If she knew. A whole fifty-seven minutes he spent in the bathroom this morning. Polishing teeth and shoes; making a tiny rip in his shirt on the left shoulder.

'Where.'

'Oh….' Andy knows she won't be lying on his tangerine designer quilt any time soon. It'll have to be somewhere really special. Somewhere the pooros and migros can't get into. Think, think. Suddenly his brother's fat face pops into his head.

'Vegas, Vegas,' he announces. He holds his breath. There are the public halls of the Super Casino $$$$$ where any old Ned with a wallet full of credit can go and drink Scottails by the glass, and then there's Vegas, Vegas, the VIP section. It's where footballers and managers and models and reality sex show stars go; where people are bankrupted in one night. Someone even hanged himself in the toilets in the first week when they lost their life savings at the American roulette table. It was almost enough to get the place shut down. But the government and the Po-Mo Corp made a joint announcement: 'This is a very regrettable incident, but we cannot remove freedom of choice from the ordinary citizen.' So Vegas, Vegas remained open, occupying one floor — the penthouse. And it gleams across the Clyde, a yellow hum of sequins and money on a grey night.

'You can get in there?' Mischa asks. Her look says she doesn't believe him.

For once, Andy is grateful that his stupid pig of a brother is a bouncer. Not that he'll tell her that. Oh no, let her think he's a man of surprises. 'If you don't fancy it…'

'I'll think about it.'

He walks back to the Po-Mo Café, punching the air.

The afternoon drags. A customer complaining that his socks unravelled at the heel; a Chinese family who buy one of every item in every colour. And the usual addicts coming in, desperate to buy something, anything, with their loose change. Cash is the mark of a destitute man in these times. He is glad when he hears a smattering of applause. It means the fountain show has started. Water cascading — purple and green — amid fairy lights and harp music to revive the weary. The smell of freshly cut lawns pumped through the scenters.

At five thirty, he's having his hot chocolate break, when she comes in with the girls from Wal-Mart. There she is, amid a knot of them. Looking at him, giggling. What was

it with girls? Why did they always do that when they fancied you? She was probably asking their advice about the date. Pointing him out. They'd tell her not to go; the bitches. He gulps the drink down so fast it burns his tongue. When he looks up, she is standing there.

'Night, Andy. Pick me up here at nine.'

'When?'

'Nine?' she enunciates in the voice people use on migros when they think they haven't understood.

'What day?'

The Wal-Mart girls collapse in a fit of laughter. He wishes their cheap blouses would rip at the seams. He wishes the whole damn mall would blow up. OK, maybe not blow up exactly. A cigarette alarm could go off.

'Tonight,' Mischa replies.

He runs home. God, I'm unfit, he thinks. But he gets there just as his brother is on his way out.

'Favour…,' he pants. 'Tonight….Hot date….Vegas, Vegas...' The last part is more of a question and he can tell from the smirk on Ben's face what the answer is.

'No way. You're under age. You can't come in unaccompanied. I'm not losing my job so you can get laid.'

'What if I come in with someone legit?'

'Still at my discretion.' (The fool can't even pronounce the word. He makes it rhyme with secretion). 'Got to go.'

'Wait! I'll give you anything you want.'

'You haven't got anything I want. Money? Yeah right. Girls? I'll get my own thanks.'

Andy wants to land a punch on Ben's gerbil face. 'What about the jacket?' he shouts, triumphant.

'What jacket?'

'THE jacket.'

They both know. The green pleather first-day-of-the-sale-queue-up-outside-in-the-pissing-rain jacket. They both wanted it so bad. It was the last one and full price it would have cost three months' wages. It would have been every birthday and Christmas present for the next two years.

'It could be my Bar Mitzvah gift. I never

got a Bar Mitzvah gift,' Andy pleaded with his dad.

'You're not Jewish!'

'That's just discrimination.'

In the end, Andy got it. Of course he got it. He let his brother stand in line for it. Then when Ben ran through the shop doors (breaking one of the retail records for speed), skidding like a mad thing, there was Andy, holding it high above his head. He'd found himself a job in the shop the week before. It was the start of his Employment in The Retail Sector. He thought Ben was going to explode.

Andy loves that jacket. But it's the only thing he has to bargain with. Mischa better be worth it. She'll have to date him for at least six weeks.

'Well?'

Ben gives Andy a playful cuff on the head. 'Put the jacket in my wardrobe, turn up with a grown-up and you got yourself a deal.'

Andy slaps more cologne on his face, slicks back his red hair.

Uncle Zorba takes one more puff of his cigar. 'God, I wish they'd un-ban smoking,' he says. 'I know it's bad for you but still…. Ready to go, Andy?'

His uncle started the 'Put the glass back in Glasgow' campaign and everyone seemed to have forgotten he was responsible for the original 'Take the glass out of Glasgow' campaign. It made him a millionaire in 2007. (He was the city's prime supplier of plastic cups). The first time round, they told him Plasto was helping the nation. He got free drinks in every bar in the West End. 'You won't remember this, you were too wee,' his mam tells him, 'but your Uncle Zorba crossed picket lines to get his plastic cups in the bars when the law changed.' He had a good run. He beat down the wine connoisseurs, the restaurateurs, all the people who said you'd ruin good alcohol by serving it in plastic. The students were a big help. He bribed them with free drinks to petition for him. Then the Green Party had a surge in popularity and plastic was the bad guy again. But Uncle Zorba had sold out before that. So now glass is back. And what do you know? Zorba owns Glass rite (the city's

prime supplier of glass glasses).

It's five past nine and the sunset has just started in the mall. The false sky is turning lemon and apricot. In another hour, the moon and stars will be out in the Po-Mo firmament. She's there by the Café. Trim, hands in the pockets of her black coat. Her hair piled on top of her head in a cone, like a movie star.

'Great looking lassie,' Uncle Zorba mutters. 'If I was ten years younger….Close your mouth, Andy. You look like a bleedin' goldfish.'

He is introducing them; Zorba's kissing her hand. Andy winces, but Mischa doesn't seem to mind. Her eyes look huge; her skin delicate. He knows he is staring again at those pink shiny lips. When will he get a chance to kiss her? They don't speak in the car as they roll through the city. The city the Tourist Board call Shoppers' Heaven.

Here it is. The Clyde's multi-billion pound controversy. The Super Casino $$$$$ sign flashes red neon and the queue is already trailing three blocks. The biggest gambling palace in the whole of the U.K. Of course it's not anywhere as big as the U.S. ones. There are hotels there with ten thousand rooms. Vegas, Vegas has its own entrance. A gilt door to an elevator that whisks you up, up the outside of the building, till the river seems far below. And at the door is a man in a tight-fitting suit. The look on Ben's face is worth any green pleather jacket.

'All right, Uncle Zorb,' the oaf says. 'Who's this babelicious goddess?'

She giggles. 'Mischa. You're Andy's brother, right?'

Andy turns to her in amazement. 'How did you know that?'

'You look identical,' she shrugs.

He isn't sure who's more annoyed, him or Ben. But Ben is leering, using that voice he copied off some cop show where handsome vigilantes are always beating up paedophiles: 'Well, Mischa, I'm going to have to get you to take off that coat. Just to check you're…suitably attired.'

The lech. The dirty lech, man. But Mischa smiles sweetly (she can't be falling for him. Please don't say she's falling for him):

'No problem. I wanted Andy to see my new dress anyhow. Close your eyes,' she orders.

So he waits, as she wriggles her arm out of one sleeve, then another. Silence.

'Open.'

He blinks. And her dress...what a dress. What…a…dress….It's blue velveteen and ends mid-thigh. And in bold canary yellow fluorescent print across her chest…

'What's up, Andy?' Mischa smirks.

'You….You're wearing that?'

'You could always put the coat back on,' Ben offers, his gaze on Mischa's long, oh so long, legs.

Andy snaps. 'You'll have to change.'

She yawns: 'Won't I get in like this?'

'I'd love to get you out of it,' Ben winks.

Zorba stamps his feet. He hates the outdoors. It's too cold. 'What are we waiting for?'

She has to change. Has to. Standing there with her coat over one arm and that dress. That dress…blue velveteen…bold canary yellow fluorescent print across her chest…that says…that says…IKEA?!? What was she thinking? 'Put your coat on,' Andy hisses.

Mischa takes one look at him. 'That's why I never bothered with you before, Andy Scott. You're shallow as puddles.'

And with that, she grinds her glass-tipped shoe into his foot and walks away into the crisp night.

Marie-Anne Mancio has a doctorate in Live Art and lectures for Tate Modern's online contemporary art course. 'She Wore Blue Velveteen' was written in response to a Glasgow 2020 event held in the Love Café in Govan. She is currently writing her first novel.

†

ALLOWED, ABLE AND WILLING

— John Daly

9am Monday May 18 2020
Class 1G
2 hour question time

Joe looked out the classroom window to distract himself with the busy traffic on the Clyde. He had been thinking too much about tonight's meeting and it made him feel anchored to an unhappy time.

He spotted The Learning Boat pulling out of the dock below the school. It was full to its barge-shaped gunnels with pupils and a few staff, heading upriver towards the new Independence Bridge. Everyone sat on the top deck in neat little clusters of eight. The boat disappeared for a moment behind the Cruising Café, which was doing its usual, aimlessly drifting about on the water. He could see the suits and sunglasses sat at tables on its open deck, their laptops and newspapers flashing open in the sun.

His eyes widened as a huge salmon leapt clean out the water. Its silver bar glistened in the sun for a long second before the spectacular splash punched a big hole in the reflected building across the water. Two seconds later another huge fish splashed in the water, just beyond the rank of taxi-boats. Joe stared into the shattered reflections on the Clyde as the images melted away then reformed again. He felt trapped.

It would be his turn for a day on the learning cruiser next week, he reassured himself. Maybe take the fishing rod. The thought cheered him up and he made a wish for the weather to be as hot as today's, another new record for high temperatures in May, they said on the news this morning.

'Sir, Sir, whit time dae we send ur votes in the day?' squealed Neelam, high and loud enough to be heard over the classroom noise and to drag Joe's mind out of the river.

'That's in yer Googlebox Neelam, just ask it. And class! It's too loud, Keep the Hum Down!'

'Sir, do you get a vote on this wan?'

115

Asked Jude from the other side of the circle. Like everyone else, she was slumped forward on the desk, hands holding either side of the Gbox, the thumbs doing all the work. Joe's sat down at his desk, which was also part of the circle.

'Yes, yes,' Said Joe, 'course I do. Everyone's got a vote oan this issue. It's an important choice that affects everyone and not just you. Remember, this is fur all Scottish schools. It's the furst time that…it's History in the making…'

'Sur, we know aw that,' shouts Ross as the class hums louder with excitement. 'It's aw o'er the news. We seen the camera crews everywhere. Seen the BBC van outside? There's loads o' thum. Neelam even goat interviewed fur the radio Sur. Didn't ye Neelam?'

The class cheers. 'So we're no' daft, Sur,' concluded Ross, without once looking up from the World War game he was winning, again, with the use of just two, slightly larger than normal, thumbs.

'…It's the most important vote you've hud this year. Maybe, the most important you'll ever huv. Ye all really understand whit this means though class? Do you? You've hud the vote on lots of issues since you've been in this school, bit you're only furst years and jist a few years ago, I mean, it wis unheard of to allow kids tae decide important issues in school. And this….This is politics. Do you know how privileged you are?'

Nobody seemed to be listening, till eventually Ross chips in.

'Aye, Sur, we know democracy works. Is it a privilege though, Sur, or…' his mind still fixed on the war game, his body shaking and his thumbs going flat out. 'DIE! DIE! DIE!' His body slumps back in defeat and he sighs, '…or a right, Sur?' Lifting his eyes to Joe sat there looking confused, he didn't wait for an answer, but followed up with 'Bit whit ur you voting fur, Sur?'

'None o' yer business. Fed up telling yeez. So! Voting's at 3 class. The ballot code will be emailed to everyone at 2.55 and you'll have 5 minutes to cast yer votes. Right, whose gonna give me a good question?'

'But Sir,' pleaded Sam, 'it's awfy hard tae think up questions that urney in the Gbox.'

'Aye, it's tough, but important. It's important you learn to ask questions, difficult questions, questions aboot life, philosophy and, and, and art. The things we don't know. The things that keep changing. It gies us teachers something worthwhile to do and it reminds you that the incredible Gbox disnae quite know everything. Yes, Kane?'

'Sir, whit's a Ned? NAW! Naw, I've asked that afore. Sir, when's a good time tae start sexual relations wi sum wun?'

'That again Kane? You get points for good questions Kane. Questions that've been asked hunners o' times don't get good points.'

From the other end of the circle Billy came in with, 'Sir, how long huv these Googleboxes been around?'

'That answer's in Googlebox! Jeeez! Look it up Billy. Here.' Joe grabs his own Googlebox from his desk, holding one of the keys down he speaks into the Googlebox in a flat voice. 'Question: How long, has Googlebox, been used, in education?'

Joe, holding the box to his ear like the old mobile phones, paraphrases what he's hearing.

'Since 2007, we've had them. You were the test school, guinea pigs. Modern Secondary in Glasgow. Every Scottish school since 2009 has them. The ones you have are the latest models, and, the best yet, the easiest to use. Blah, blah, blah.'

He was relieved that the IT hadn't let him down, as it often done before. If IT don't work, you lose the class in seconds. All the teachers know that. Joe was pleased with himself, until he tried to close the Scottish Ocean Band Link, or SOB, before the sponsorship jingle kicked in. Panicking, he pressed half the buttons, but everyone got the unmistakable first few bars of 'Hurrah! Hurrah! We are PC World….' Joe dropped his box down on his desk knowing that it might be days before he got that tune out of his head again.

'Sur, whit does GDP mean? Ah've just downloaded ma news page here, in it says that Scotland's goat the highest GDP in the world. Is that good Sir or bad Sir?'

The School on the Opposite Bank
of the Clyde
9am Monday May 18 2020
Class 1W

Mike looked out of his classroom window. He could see the other school across the Clyde. It reflected his own in almost every way; made of glass, steel and silvery alloy, cubes and modules of various shapes, with hundreds of tiny windmills on the roof. It too was now twice the size of the original building. The schools were constantly adding bits to themselves hidden beneath veils of scaffolding and canvas adverts for Scottish Water and Scot iT.

Mike's class were settling in to their circle of desks. He ignored them and the life flowing past on the river and stared at the school opposite his. He was running his finger along the outline of a deep scar in his forehead. It started just above his right eyebrow, then curved and narrowed as it swept upwards and across and was so like the famous sportswear tick that the school just had to nickname him Nike, or, quite often, Spikey Nike because of his snippy attitude. When he was a younger man he could partially hide the scar behind his fringe, but now, hair much thinner and cropped short, he was beginning to look like one of those Glasgow hard men you never see anymore. Rubbing his scar with his index finger helped Mike relax and think.

He'd been thinking about it a lot recently, this scar, what it means to him, where it came from, what it's made him. Tonight, he hoped to get some answers. That's why he instigated the meeting. He was excited about the prospect like going on a first date. Tonight's the night, after what, eighteen months of waiting, applications, forms and interviews, waiting, counselling and waiting? Ah'm so ready fur this he mused. What'll he be like, this guy? He's agreed tae see me, but does he remember whit he did tae me? Whit does he think noo? Ah've carried this since Ah wis fourteen and jist because of what? Because of what? That's what I want to know. Is he still a Ned, an old Ned? I hope he's a nothing, unemployed, uneducated, barely alive, scumbag, down-an-out waster. Ah hope he's goat cancer.

'Sir, Sir what time's the vote today?' Asked Jamie.

'The vote? Oh aye, the vote.' Mike stopped the rubbing but continued his staring out the window. as he muttered, 'Yes, it's 3.'

'Sir,' Jamie continued, 'whit you voting Sir?'

'It's a private vote, so none of your damn business Jamie boy. Naebody explain the rules of school democracy to you yet?'

'Aye bit Sir, the news says it's gonna be a landside anyway. 75 to 25, they just said that oan the news this morning. Ye see the cameras ootside Sir?'

'Aye, if the polls are accurate, which they seldom are. And there's ey camras ootside cause we're just next door to the BBC and STV and aw they media liberal, wish washy...We'll jist have to wait and see. Won't we?'

Mike was not in the mood for two hours of questions, especially from this class with its more than fair share of smart Alecs. He was increasingly feeling bad this morning. Late night last night. Felt he had to do something that involved tradition and nostalgia, so he and a few old pals watched old football DVDs and got drunk and sang loud songs seldom heard. It was great at the time, he thought. But now?

He remembered the rant to his mates last night. 'I used tae like teaching when Ah furst started in 2007. You'd the freedom to teach as you saw fit without all this IT stuff, getting in ma way. Ah'm telling ye, it started wi gieing thum a say and a vote on how they were taught and how they rated us, the teaching. Now, they're running the show, and thur getting bloody paid for it. Paid for learning? Why should the school be payin thum tae learn? Ah don't get it. It's no right.'

What about me, he thought, what about my feelings? They're in charge now and they film and record every word you say with those wretched boxes. You so much as shout at someone and there's fifteen witnesses all saying you've broken the rules and they've all got proof to back it up. You've no chance. I used to just get them through the exams, teach them what they need to know, and I was bloody good at that. Now I'm required to make them laugh and enjoy learning at the same time or else they mark me down! I'm no' a fucking comedian. They get paid and everyone passes everything with flying colours and I get a shitty C for English fur fuck's sake, C for effort and attitude and a D for sense of humour!

'Right Class, TURN IT DOWN!. Now, that's better, give us your questions. YOU!'
'Sur, is it true Glasgow's just bin voted the happiest City in Europe?'

Joe's Class

Joe was trying to tell them about the Googlebox being the best thing ever for schools and how its introduction directly led to the education revolution. But that just set the class off into a big argument about what is the best thing about education. Joe let them run at it for a while enjoying the learning process in action, the curiosity, the difference of opinions, the ding-dongs, the growth, the change, watching them tearing into a subject to find its truth. After a while the class united to disagree with Joe. It wasn't the Gbox that made the biggest difference to education. According to them it was paying groups of kids for their learning. Then they started to teach themselves. 'The more you learn the more we earn.'

'Sir, how did people discover thit we wur much better at the teaching than adults?'
'Good point Amelia. Yes, better teachers? Ha ha ha! You're quite confident aboot that, eh?...Ah guess you're right Amelia. You do more or less all the teaching yourselves now. It wis gradual really. Amelia, you know, a wee bit at a time. We started with looking at whit got in the way of learning. We used tae think thit children jist wurney willing to learn. At best, no' able. Bit when we discovered they wurney allowed to learn, schools actually gitting in the way of learning, well that changed everything. And now look! So Aye, we just backed off a bit and let you take over a bit, that's how it aw started.'

He looked around the class and noticed they were nearly all staring into their Googleboxes with the same faint smile on their faces, clearly not listening to him. The Learning Hum was a nice medium Joe thought. When it gets too high you know they're up to something. Too low, they're bored. He was getting used to it. Good at it.

The one thing he couldn't get used to was when they start looking you up on the Teachers' Registers, checking out your details then firing the questions at you from all directions. 'Is that aw ye could score in the Student/Staff Feedback last term Sir? No' very good on the old attendance performance are you Sir? Missed a few Mondays there, Sir. Nothing tae fur Extra Curricular Activities and didnae even score anything under the "Injects Humour and Fun into Learning" column! Sir, ur you sure ye want to be a teacher?'

One not staring or muttering into his Gbox was Tam Hope. He sat staring out the window up river towards the old Graving Dock in Govan. He could just see the old derelict wheelhouse, or what's left of it, covered in generations of graffiti. He tried to visualise it as it would have been 30 or 40 years ago when the ships queued to berth for repair. Hundreds, thousands of men climbing over the steel hulls, all made to look the same by the grimy, greasy dirt. He closed his eyes and thinking of old news clips he'd seen and stories heard from his dad and granddad, he imagined what it must have been like then, for them, with the deafening noise, the dirt, the constant dangers, the sparks and flashes, the humour and camaraderie, the hard graft, the smells, the poisoned fumes and smoke and the deadly dust hanging in the air. Thank fuck, he thought to himself, Ah'll never bae daen anything like that when Ah leave school. He looked up the water and saw the Finneston crane sticking out from the new generation, the Armadillo, the Tower, the Science Centre, the new BBC, and Media Village, the cafés and restaurants, like a grandfather at a teenager's party.

Tam could see Joe was looking at him. 'Ma turn Sur? Yes, the Gbox, it might've got kids tae become better learners, Sur. I mean, it cut oot the middlemen, the teachers, dint it? So we learn whit we want how we want. That's good. But, Sur, dae you really think it's good for people to be so, like, digitised? I mean, wur aw talking like robots noo and rather than mix wi friends and family, wur communicating only wi people we'll probably niver meet. Our relationships huv been digitised, Sir? What de ye think?'

Joe was getting used Tam's questions in this class. Probably his big brother's or his Dad's really. 'Is that your question Thomas?'.

'No Sur, tell me Sur, cause this answer definitely isn't in the Gbox, how should I vote next week? You tell me what you think I should do and why?'

Joe tried to explain why he couldn't, but the class rounded on him firing difficult questions and, sensing his difficulty, took control of the debate, which was close to becoming a trial. He knew it was a wind up but he couldn't escape.

'Sir, Dae ye still support any o' the Old Firm? When was the last time ye went tae the Chapel? Are you one of those Orange men who March around the park once a year? What do you think the result will be? Will you be happy if it's Aye? Will ye leave if it's Naw? Howzyergranny? Sir? She on the level?'

Joe felt like he was suffocating, lacking the witty comebacks to stop seeming dull and stupid. He was trying to think of a killer joke but couldn't. He couldn't shout over them. Tam came in for the kill.

'Sir, this class is for stuff we cannae find oot in Gbox, right? So if ye cannae teach us stuff in this class, important stuff like what we should vote for the future of Scottish schools, then whit are ye fur? Sur?'

The calls came quick and fast. 'Sir, we'll respect you more if we know what you vote. C'mon, we'll all tell you what we're voting, won't we class? It's democracy! C'mon! Aye or Naw? Aye or Naw? Aye or Naw?'

Joe tried to tell them without telling them by saying he knew the vote was a foregone conclusion. He knew how they were going to vote. They'd been telling their teachers for months and pupil's pre-election polls show an 85% landslide. He can see the headline: 'SCOTTISH SCHOOLS VOTE FOR UNITY'.

In desperate defence Joe thought of something smart to try. 'You've been listening to your Dad again Thomas. Haven't you? Now you want me to tell you how to vote. Why don't you think for yourself?'

'My Dad said you'd say that.'

Joe couldn't hold back anymore with Thomas. 'Ask your Dad if he'd like tae go back to the old days, when he was at school? 9 till 4, five days a week, without the chance to earn good money and learn what he wanted at the same time? Probably being whacked by leather belts for not following orders? Sitting exams every other week, being bullied and made tae feel guilty fur doing well? Ask him.'

'Yes, but ma Dad did awright in spite o' that. Got him a good job wi a trade in the Yards. He said that aw this computer stuff and that Second Scottish Enlightenment shite is rubbish coz it's just for people who don't mix, for people that prefer machines to people. It stops us mixing, IT does.'

No one else seemed to be listening to them.

'I take it this is your question for today Thomas, because I haven't got the time to go into...Listen, before the digital revolution and the education revolution in Scotland we didney have hundreds of thousands of families queuing to get into Scotland from all over the world to get the best education in Europe. When your dad worked in the yards, thousands of families were leaving Scotland, not queuing up tae get in. Whit's your Dad doing now? He's not in the Yards is he? Naw, because there urney any! In his day we didnae huv success rates at school thit broke the scales....'

Joe could hear the words 'His Dad's DEAD' come from somewhere in the class but he didn't know where and besides it doesn't matter because all that mattered now was finishing what he was saying while thinking of what next to say to Thomas — now that his Dad is dead! Jesus, when did his Dad die? Who's asking these questions then?

'...Who would've thought that 2nd year pupils would be employed to teach 1st years, even ten years ago? Two hours wi a teacher fur every six hours of team learning and schools have been transformed, into, into, eh…'

Joe was looking at Tam now, confused and wishing the ground would open up, and Tam stared back. Silence.

'My Dad died on the last day of work in the last day of the last shipyard on the Clyde. A freak accident it was. A big heavy, rusty spike. Went right through…'

'Sir, Sir,' burst Sophie's voice into the circle, 'is it true the top pupil earner in the school last year cleared fourteen thousand euros?'

'No, it was eighteen. Two thousand in tax,' answered Jamie from across the circle. 'But that was exceptional. That student doesn't do anything ever good for anyone but himself. He's in my sister's class and he's a bit weird. Name's Anthony Thatcher.'

'You're well informed.' Said Joe, smiling. He looked at Tam who was now looking out the window. He hoped to just drop the subject of his dad if Tam and the class would let him. They seemed to, at first. Joe promised himself to take it easy on Tam and make up for his error and lack of tact. Then the class burst into laughter.

From somewhere he heard the words, 'Tell him the truth, Sur, Sur, he's no deed. Works in PC World.' More laughter.

Joe's head was spinning. He stood still unable to decide what to do next. For once everyone looked at him, apart from Tam. The class calmed down to a silence in anticipation. Joe took a deep breath, scanned the circle, 'Okay. Got me. Move on. Jamie?'

Jamie continued to impress with his research. Reading from his Gbox on his lap, 'The average earnings though, for first years, is twelve hundred euros; second years two k; third years four; fourth years six fifty and fifth years nine fifty. The lowest in the school was not below fifteen percent of the average…Gavin Burns got a special ten thousand Euro bonus for creating a surplus of school energy after connecting two hundred exercise bikes to the supply. Now, with the windmills and solar panels, the school sells energy to the national grid. All proceeds will go of course into our wage packets at the end of the year.'

'Okay, Okay, very good. Your big sister's obviously been teaching you the benefits of the Gbox Jamie. Right next question.'

The rest of the questions came quickly since almost all of them were answered by Jamie's Googlebox. 'When did pupils take control of schools? Why did Googlebox create a revolution in education and communication? Are you married Sir? Where do you think I should go on holiday? What team will win the European Elite League this year? Why don't the teachers spend more time on the power bikes making electricity? How many companies does the school service for IT and Accountancy? Why does the Art department make more money than the engineering? Why is Glasgow now the Capital of Scotland?

'Now then, a few minutes left so I'll give ye the class feedback in a few moments — first, I'd like tae say well done tae everyone for mastering the new teacher scoring system and getting the projects in on time. And also, well done with no-one, at all, failing.' A small cheer goes up in the class.

'Sir, Sir, have we earned a lot? Can you show us how the points system works?'

'I'll show you in good time. Or you can ask Jamie after class. He probably knows. Everyone go tae the Email folder now and download the personal, team and class results and save them in yer Points folder. Once again, well done class. A good score for 1st year. If you keep this up you'll be in the Euro Express Gold Card class by fourth year. Now, good luck to those taking part in the press conference today. Do yourselves and the class proud.'

For a minute Joe felt good after class then his heart sank as he remembered tonight's meeting.

Mike's class

For twenty minutes the class had been fiercely debating the merits of voting 'YES' or 'NO' in the ballot. Mike was getting more and more unhappy and the noise in the class was getting louder and louder and about to meet Mike head-on as he reached the point where self control gives way to emotional anarchy.

'STOP! TURN IT DOWN WILL YOU?' Silence. Mike caught himself and took a deep breath. He relaxed and reminded himself that shouting is okay in cases where you can't be heard. 'Next question, please!'

He dealt with the usual wacky stuff you get from 1st years, most of it they could've got from the Gbox if they asked it the right way, but that's okay with Mike because it saves him the bother. Sir, is thur a God? Sir, when did the student's revolution take place? Why dae the teachers hate us calling it a revolution? Whose gonna win at fitbaw the night? Whit's a Ned, Sur? What's it like Sur to huv gone tae School withoot getting paid? (The class always laughs at this question.) How much money does the school make fae businesses?

But the one that really got his goat was the question 'Sir, dae ye think yer a better teacher than the Gbox?'

He'd been a teacher for thirteen years and was forced to watch as his role changed beyond recognition. He was no longer the storekeeper supplying the goods. He was the doorman to the store. Children have access now to more information than a billion teachers could supply. How do you compete with that? These damn Gboxes have everything in them. Songs, films, games, books, exams, results, everyone's scores, pay, performance and behaviour records, telephone, video camera, email, internet, voting box, chat and learning forums. How can they fail?

Mike didn't give up. 'Can the Gbox teach you how to be good? No. Can it teach you how to play football? No? Does it teach you how to survive in the jungle out there? Naw. For that you need...'

'But Sir, whit jungle? We don't live in a jungle.'

'Does it teach you whit facts to believe? How dae you know if any of it's true or not? That's where teachers come in.'

'Sur, we can work it out oorsels.'

'You need us teachers to run things.'

'But Sir, schools are run by us now,' chimed Ken unaware he was the back breaking straw.

'YOU?' He shouted, pointing and jabbing his finger at the shocked little boy. 'SCHOOLS ARE RUN BY YOU UR THEY? YOU'RE A LITTLE FURST YEAR. WHIT DAE YOU KNOW ABOUT RUNNING A SCHOOL? YOU'RE JIST IN THE DOOR FOR GOD'S SAKE! WHAT KIN YOU DO? EH? YOU'RE NOT SMART ENOUGH TO LOOK EFTER YERSELF, SO HOW KIN YE LOOK EFTER A SCHOOL? TELL ME!'

Ken started to cry.

'You're oot o' order Sir,' said Amber holding her Gbox in her right hand like a police badge, its camera pointing straight ahead. 'He said 'we' were running the school not him and he's right. We do run it now. Remember, we employ you. That's the deal.'

7pm Sectarian reconciliation session

The mediator introduced herself as Ms Olsen then asked Joe and Mike to introduce themselves. The three of them sat on comfy chairs with a pot of tea and three cups on the wooden coffee table between them. They chatted a while about the results of the vote today and all agreed that 92% in favour of One State One School was a shock. It was also a shock to them when they discovered they both worked as teachers on the opposite sides of the Clyde. The mediator couldn't stop them breaking confidentiality. It just came out. After that they disagreed on most issues concerning the vote, like, will the transformation be a problem? Will more people opt for home education now? Was it a result due to government brainwashing and propaganda? Is it a good thing at all?

The mediator had to calm things down and moved them on to talk about the event that's brought them here today. Joe explained his part by talking about youth culture, gang culture as it was then. How he'd been caught up in the raw excitement, the street fighting, the football, the stones and bottles being thrown, the chases, the police, the cell, the court appearance, the fear and the responsibility, the probation officer taking an interest, going the extra yard for him, lending him books to read, the workmate that helped him into college, the change in direction. The guilt.

Mike talked about his gang. It was the same story, just a different football team and patch of Glasgow. He described the slow motion detail of having a broken glass pushed into your face. He spoke of the frustration he felt when the court dishes out probation for the wilful attack that could have blinded him and has left him with this ugly reminder. He revealed how he'd grown out of running with the gangs when he met his first wife Janet. She'd brought out a better side to Mike and managed to tame his aggression by being impressed not by violence and machismo but by maturity and qualifications.

The mediator brought the two stories together in a nice neat wee parcel. Then Ms Olsen indicated that the two-hour session was over and they all stood up. Joe was smiling and looked relaxed. So seemed Mike, as he held his hand out to shake Ms Olsen's, then, looking Joe in the eyes, took his hand in both of his, warmly shaking it for much longer than Joe felt comfortable with. Joe liked what he was hearing but Mike's stare was a little too intense, as if he was holding back something with great effort.

'It wis so good to do this. So weird that you work across the river from me too . They'll probably huv tae build a new bridge 'tween thum noo. But I'm glad I've done it, got in touch and that, heard your story. Never thought you'd be a teacher too. Strange. Yeah, Ah'm glad 'ave done it, met you. Teacher, eh? But Ah'm eh, gonna be leaving soon. Taking a job down south in London. They're aw coming up here, Ah know, begging tae work, but I like tae be different. Plus ave goat a good promotion and that. Charge o' a department.'

'That's great,' said Joe, 'when will you be leaving? Ahh, next term start. That's good. Well big changes in Scotland coming up for the next year. So eh, yeah, well…'

'We should meet up fur a drink or something before Ah go,' smiled Mike.. 'Would be good to hear more from you. What dae ye say? Now Ah know where ye ur, Ah can get a hold of you quite easy.'

'Yeah, you do that,' said Joe.

John Daly is a facilitator and worked with 101 Dimensions on Glasgow 2020. 'Allowed, Able and Willing' was written directly as a result of John's experience of facilitating a number of Glasgow 2020 events. His life story from the Govan shipyards to someone drawn to questions about philosophy and change mirrored the city's wider experience. This is his first published story.

†

A TALE OF TWO CITIES

— Kirsten Anderson

So you're on your way hame. Having to go through this palaver at your time of life. It's just no right. No that it's anything new, mind. You've been putting up with this for 5 years. And the thing that gets you is that everyone seems to love it! They cannae stop raving about it. This new Glasgow. But you cannae stop thinking back to the good old days when you just had to hop onto the no 203 and it would take you right to Gorbals Leisure Centre, 2 minutes from your house. Easy. You did that for nearly forty years and it suited you just fine thank you very much. But now? Well half of the bus routes have been cancelled, and in their place you've got trams, light railways and water taxis. Water taxis! If someone had told you fifteen years ago that you'd be getting a water taxi hame you'd have laughed in their face. You'd heard all the rumblings about Clydeside Regeneration. Your pals at the Council said it was going to happen. But you didnae actually believe it. Pie in the sky pipe dreams. That's what you said when you heard about it. And that's what you secretly hoped. That it would all come to nothing. You're no a big fan of change. If it ain't broke and all that. Ok, maybe Glasgow was a wee bit broken. But you liked it that way. They should have left well enough alone.

It's no that you're moaning. You're no. You're all for helping out the environment. You just don't see why they had to stop all those buses. Aye, the water taxis take the same routes but they should still have left folk with a choice. They could at least have kept the no 203. And you're no just saying that 'cos it was your bus. You're no. It was a popular route, that's all. But they did away with it and now the quickest way hame for you is the bloody water taxi. You're a terra firma type thank you very much but if you want to get hame you've no other choice. Apart from walking. And you're no a huge fan of walking on account of you getting out of puff so easily. The doc says you need to lose weight but he must say that to everyone 'cos Glasgow may be all slick and streamlined now but the folk that live here sure as hell arenae. It's the skinny kid that gets picked on in the Glasgow playgrounds these days, no the fat one. So, aye you probably should walk and burn off the steak pie supper you had at lunch. But what with your joints you'll no take the risk.

Bloody water taxi! You cannae get a seat. What a palaver. And before anyone says anything, you know it's good that the Clyde isnae just lying there doing nothing any more. But just look what they've done to it. Back in the day, the Clyde was a man's river. Ship building and industry. That's what the Clyde was famous for. That's what made this city and its people. Good decent working class folk. And aye they were tough times but it wasnae all doom and gloom. You can testify to that. It's what the likes of Billy Connolly's humour was built on after all. His days in the Finnieston shipyards. No wonder he's buggered off to the States. Look at what the Clyde's subjected to these days; poncey water taxis and café bars and posh hotels and galleries all along the banks. No very manly is it? You'll no be seeing the next Billy Connolly being spawned from that. No the Billy from the old days anyway. Before he sold out and started writing shitey musicals for Broadway. The Yanks think he's something but you're getting sick to the back teeth of trying to explain what a jobbie is to tourists. It's no like they're floating in the Clyde any more and you can just point one out. Imagine writing a musical with Jobbie in the title. Pretending he's still down to earth and in touch with his roots when he hasnae been here for years and wouldnae know a jobbie if it hit him in the face. Probably thinks he's too good to wipe his own arse now. So maybe Billy would be fine here after all. With all the other poncey jessies. Aye, you're living in a city full of big poncey jessies. And that's no the Glasgow you want to live in. That's no your Glasgow.

Yours was No Mean City Glasgow. Home to Taggart and Tennents and The Ice Cream Wars. Aye it had a bad reputation. But all the best people and places have an edge you know? Edinburgh was the pretty city, Glasgow the gritty city. The don't mess wi' us city. And now? Well it's all gone a step too far and quite frankly you could do without it. If you wanted to live in Paris or Venice then you would. You liked the old Glasgow. You were happy then. It wasnae perfect but it felt like home to you. It's all just changed so fast. And the crowds! You cannae move 2 feet before falling over some poncey tourists, getting in your way with their maps and their rucksacks and asking you to take photies and gushing about how lucky you must feel to live here. Aye right. Lucky's no the word. You cannae be doing with all that crap from foreigners who never wanted to come here twenty years ago. But a few new bridges and galleries and hotels and festivals and all of a sudden it's good enough? We're good enough? Well they can get tae…they can just piss off back hame. Or to Edinburgh. It used to be enough for them. Although Edinburgh doesnae have a Tate Scotland. Glasgow got it. You were glad when that happened. No because you thought Tradeston needed another poncey gallery full of sheep and formaldehyde or whatever's in the place. But just because Edinburgh assumed it would go to them. Probably thought they deserved it since we got the Commonwealth Games in 2014. Get it up ye. That's what you thought.

You didn'nae mind too much when Glasgow won the bid. You hoped The Games would be a bit like the Garden Festival in '88; a one off that would bring in a bit of money for the city. Aye, it would bring in tourists you thought, but they'd be away soon enough. But now you think that The Council must have used all that cash the Games brought in to really go for broke building this new Glasgow. So now you sometimes wonder if it would have been better if the Games had gone to somewhere else. Like Canada. Because it was around that time all the trouble seemed to start. Ever since then the tourists have been pouring in. And they're no just day trippers anymore, because whenever one festival's over another one seems to begin. And there's all these galleries and museums and more shops than you can shake a stick at. Better shopping than London some folk say. And the tourists love the fact we're now the River City. You still cannae believe that's

what the tourist board dreamt up; Glasgow — The River City. These advertising folk get paid about two hundred grand a year and that's what they come up with? River City? Is it just you, or was that no the name of some shitey soap that got axed about 15 years ago?

And the film makers. The city's teeming wi' them! Everybody wants to make their films about Glasgow these days. Or write books set in Glasgow. And you wouldnae mind so much except it's no your old Glasgow they're writing about. It's this new European Glasgow. Cosmopolitan Glasgow. You're open minded. You are. But you make a point of reading none of them. You like the old stuff. About the old Glasgow with all its flaws. It's like Glasgow's got tickets on itself these days. It's up its own backside. And that's just no right. You werenae brought up to think you were anything special. None of you were. It's no the Glasgow way is it?

You don't like to tell folk but you've gone to The Green a few times to see what all the fuss was about. Festivals on non-stop. And no just wee pishy ones like they used to have in The Merchant City. Nowadays folk come from all over the world just to be part of it all. It's mostly poncey shite of course but you thought the book festival was alright. Aye Write, it's called. You thought that was quite clever. Aye, all the biggest and best writers come to the book festival. Even the ones you like. The ones that wrote about your Glasgow. Your favourite book is *Lanark* by a bloke called Alasdair Gray. You don't tell folk though. No' 'cos you're ashamed but because you gather it's quite trendy to like this particular novel. It's one of the ones that still comes up in all these Top Ten Scottish Books events. And you're no going to be seen as jumping on any bandwagon like those arty farty arse-holes. You read that book years ago. You bought it for the cover if truth be told. It's got this weird drawing of a bloke with loads of other wee folk inside his body. And he's giant like with his crown and his swords, looming over all these buildings and landmarks, some of which you thought you recognised, some you didn't. You had to read it a few times to understand it and you're still no sure if you do. You cannae even put your finger on what you like about it. But it just gives you this feeling. Aye it may be a bit depressing but the Glasgow in this book seems more familiar to you than the one you're living in now — shiny happy Glasgow. So you dip into *Lanark* now and again and try and magic yourself into the past.

You finally get a seat. Next to a bloody foreigner of course. She's a bit of a bubble-heed. And she wants to bend your ear, like they all do. She's from New York and she's been here for 2 months as part of her university exchange programme. They must be letting anyone into universities these days. She says she's been to all the galleries and museums and been to The Green and done lots of shopping and she's had fun. But she's wondering if you'll tell her the stuff about your Glasgow. So you do. You tell her about the Gorbals, from its days as a leper colony, right through to the present. You tell her about the Shipyards, about your school-days, about your grandpa who used to light the street lamps. You tell her everything. And she listens until you stop talking.

'It's like, so totally amazing to be here', she says. 'I mean, I've been to a lot of plac-es that have been, like, modernised, you know? But they give me this weird feeling. Kinda like something's been lost. Like the spirit of the city. You know?'

'Aye', you say. But you're shaking your head. She's intae all that poncey new age shite. You can tell. A couple more minutes and she'll be talking about her past lives and asking to read your aura. Bloody hell.

'It's like, Glasgow is new but it's kinda old too. You know what I mean?'

'No really hen, no'.

'Well, it's kinda like, it looks all new, you know? But it kinda has an old soul. The people, people like you are kinda what make the city, you know? I mean I've imag-ined living here for so long. And I've seen so many films set right here by the Clyde. You know the one about the girl who owns the café bar in Tradeston and she meets the gallery guy and they fall in love?'

'No', you say. 'I'm no intae all that new stuff.'

'Oh, ok. Well it's kind of like, I've seen all these places already and I kinda had an idea of what to expect. But, like, nothing could have prepared me for this. For the people. You know? Oh, here's my stop. Gotta run!'

She gets off just in time and waves at you. But you don't wave back as you're distracted by something she said. She said she'd imagined living here. In Glasgow. That gives you a weird feeling of déjà vu or something like that. Then it hits you.

You take *Lanark* off the shelf as soon as you get in and you find the passage you're looking for:

'Glasgow is a magnificent city', said McAlpin. 'Why do we hardly ever notice that?''Because nobody imagines living here', said Thaw. 'Think of Florence, Paris, London, New York. Nobody visiting them for the first time is a stranger because he's already visited them in paint-ings, novels, history books and films. But if a city hasn't been used by an artist, not even the inhabit-ants live there imaginatively.'

You read that passage again and again until it finally sinks in. You've no allowed yourself to live in this new Glasgow, not properly, not imaginatively. You've shunned the books, the films, everything. And you're miserable. You're clinging onto a past that maybe wasn't as great as you make out. You know that. But you're scared, that's all. And you've been so angry that folk might be for-getting the Glasgow you knew that you've no noticed that it's still here. And it's no going anywhere. Aye, it may look a wee bit different but so what? It's no the galler-ies and the bars and the shops that people come here for. No really. And even if it is reading books and watching films about the new Glasgow that brings folk here, that's no what they'll take away with them. It's a bit of your Glasgow they take away.

All the same, maybe you should try moving with the times a wee bit. You did-nae like the bus that much you suppose. It did get a bit stuffy. And the water taxi drops you more or less at your door too. Aye, may-be you'll check out the new Scottish writing next time you're at the literary festival but you still don't think it would go amiss for some new books and films to be made about Glasgow before the regeneration, that's all you're saying. And you might even take in that new exhibition at the Tate Scotland but only if it's proper art. You're no entertaining any of that modern crap.

Aye, you'll make the effort. Give it all a go. But you know one thing. The day you find yourself drinking frappocinos by the Clyde with all those heed the ba' poncey jessies, is the day you'll chuck yourself in front of the nearest water taxi.

Kirsten Anderson's 'A Tale of Two Cities' was a prize winner in the Glasgow 2020 competition for Glasgow University Creative Writing Masters course students.

†

REVENGE IS BITTER

— JC McCrae

Jack slammed through the doors of the close, bursting up the stairs until he reached the top floor. He shouldered the door, ran through the house, not even saying a word to the stunned occupiers. He thought he heard a shout behind him, but already he was in the lounge, only it wasn't the lounge, it was the bedroom for a couple, rapidly waking in response to the intruder. He walked up to the window, saw the lorry parked below, the reason he had chosen this tenement. He quickly walked back to the other end of the room. He could hear the footsteps thumping on the stairs behind him as he turned and sprinted for the window, building up as much speed as he could.

In fact, he didn't need much to break the window: it was single-glazed. His body, surrounded by a cloud of broken glass, sailed out into the night. Dropping quickly, he landed on the roof of the lorry, rolled to conserve momentum, dropped off the other side to the road and started running again. A safe place was only minutes away.

The vertical cul-de-sac would give him a head-start; hardly anyone in the city had ParKours down to the art that Jack had. It came in handy in his line of work.

Now he was on West Princes Street, almost a clean run to the university — except that was just what he didn't want. They could outrun him on the flat. But in Glasgow's modern cityscape flat areas were so few and far between that was hardly ever a problem. Even now as he snaked through the streets of Woodlands he had to jump and somersault over rifts in the road, cracks that had become chasms only just small enough to jump over. Buildings that hadn't been felled in the Big Quake lay split apart or pushed together, lovers leaning on each other. Most of the area was uninhabitable. Which, of course, made it perfect for Jack. And his pursuers, too.

Jack made for a gap in a building. It was like a giant had karate-chopped down the centre of the tenement, leaving the front open to the elements. There was still wiring and piping running between the two sides. Jack leapt through the gap, jumped up to grab a pipe, swung himself up onto the first floor and kept running. The door to this particular flat had already been taken off its hinges to allow for ease of escape. Jack sped up the stairs of the close, and this time made for the roof. Scrambling up through a loft shaft, he climbed onto the top of the building, being met by the fading rays of dusk. Hearing something below, he walked over to the edge of the building that faced the road he'd just come from.

They were below, circling the street. One of them must have heard him — they had such good hearing — and turned his head upwards. Pointing so the rest could see, she said, 'Jack! We're coming to get you!'

Jack turned and ran for the opposite side. They couldn't PK like him, but they were strong, and they could climb. They'd be up here in seconds. Reaching the edge, he picked up a harness, deliberately primitive so it could be put on in a hurry. Attaching it to a climbing rope made to look like electrical cable, he quickly swung onto the line and let gravity do its job. From the top of a four-storey tenement he was swinging towards a second-storey window.

No gloves: landing would be messy if he didn't do something. He swung his legs up onto the line in front of him, hoping friction would slow him sufficiently before it ate through his trousers. It still stung, but not as much as meeting sandstone at full speed.

He reached the other side. Balancing on a ledge, he took out a knife and cut the rope. Moving as fast as he could, he edged the few metres to the window and climbed inside. Ducking down, he kept his eyes above the window ledge to check if he was still being followed.

He was. What was more, some of them had done the smart thing and ran around the streets, trying to block his escape. He didn't know if they had seen him, but he had diverted them for long enough. Now it was time to escape for real.

He tiptoed through the rest of the room, ran through the hallway and into a rear bedroom. The window was empty. He jumped through it, rolled along the roof of a shed and dropped to the ground. He vaulted the wall at the back of the 'garden' (used mainly as a place to put the bins; after years of disuse it had never been greener) and found himself in an alley that lead to West Princes Street.

That way was too dangerous; too much chance he'd meet one of them and have to run on the flat, or even worse fight them with their friends around the corner. In a split second he had vaulted the next wall and found himself in another garden. The door to the close was gone. He darted in, ran to the front of the house and exited.

Turning left, he saw his escape route in front of him. Putting on a final burst of energy, he dashed forward, crossed the road at speed (no cars these days on such ruined roads) and ran headlong into the front entrance of The Primary.

Once a primary school, the building had been converted years ago into a public house. After a few incarnations, The Primary had seemed to stick. Years of somehow managing to appeal to students, old-timers, sports fans, families and smokers all at once, it was well-established in the West End. It was also brightly lit and usually busy, even on a weekday like this one. He'd be safe here.

He stumbled into the bar, exhausted, panting. He was only wearing a dark blue T-shirt and trousers, but both were soaking in sweat and dirt. Patrons turned to look at him, temporarily stopping their conversations. He eyeballed them all, but no more than a second, then walked up to the bar. 'Pint of lager,' he breathed. The barman nodded once and went to get a glass.

There was a noise from the doorway. Jack turned to see two of them standing in the doorway; panting slightly, though not so much as him; eyes fierce with that strange mix of anger and desire he had come to recognise from across a room. One girl had a hand on the other's upper arm, holding her back. They couldn't cause a scene in here. And they knew he'd be gone by closing time, somehow. Not even bothering to taunt them by smiling, he turned back to the bar and accepted his pint, took a long sip, keeping an ear towards them to check for movement.

He looked back a minute later and they

were gone.

Work done for the night.

He was quiet as a mouse coming in, but somehow she heard him anyway. When he walked into the bedroom her eyes were open, looking his way. He smiled at her.

She didn't smile back. 'What have you been doing?'

He came over and sat on the bed next to her. 'Running.' He reached out and stroked her hair. 'Nothing you wouldn't approve of.'

'I'm not a fan of running.'

'I'm not a fan of being chased.' He rubbed her shoulder briefly, then stood and stretched. 'I need a shower.' He started to head for the bathroom.

'The pipe's broken,' she called after him. The Clyde's water was still far too dirty to use for bathing, so the boathouse had water piped from the dockside. Intermittently.

'What now?'

'Got broken in the wind today.' Ever since the Gulf Stream had started to go Wonky — not reverse, just Wonky — the UK's weather had gone haywire. Gales followed cloudless days, which were followed by tornadoes. So far Glasgow was the only major city to be affected in a major way, but it was only a matter of time. 'There's enough in the tank to wash your face.'

'No, I won't bother.' Jack came back over to the bed. 'Think you can cope with me smelly?'

This time she did smile. 'I'll live. Come here.'

He crawled into bed and into her arms. A minute later he was sound asleep. She held him a minute, then scooted down so her head lay on his shoulders. She remained awake a few minutes longer, then joined him.

Jack strolled around the new place, inspecting every inch. 'Are we wired?' he asked.

Mick showed him the viewscreen of his iPalm. A webpage was clearly visible. 'We're piggybacking from the university. Two gigs. Should be enough for our purposes.'

'How much did we salvage from the old place?'

'All of the equipment. You did a good job. We were out with time to spare.'

'Well, I should hope so: I used up one of my routes in Woodlands.' After they found an escape route, the others always blocked it up somehow: putting in a security door, bricking up a window — sometimes just putting furniture in a room. If you were going to run and live, you needed to know your route. So once a route was used up, you never went back to it again. If you were smart.

Mick turned away. 'There's a 'cast I think's about you.'

That caught Jack's attention. 'Show me.'

Mick threw him the iPalm. 'It's bookmarked as questionmark-Jack.'

Jack found it. The Channel 4 cast started playing at a marked time interval:

The bodies of two women were found in south Glasgow today bearing the typical markings of a ritual killing. The women, as yet to be identified, were decapitated and their bodies mutilated. The bodies were found at approximately seven-thirty this morning. A police spokesman called the killings 'Brutal', and urged anyone with information to come forward. Because of the ritualistic nature of the murders, the case is being passed on to the NOK unit of Strathclyde police.

After that, the cast went on to some other story.

Jack switched it off and tossed it back to Mick. 'What makes you think it was me?'

Mick smiled. 'Come on, boy, we know we're not the only group you run with.'

Another of the cell, Thom, walked in. 'Is this about the 'cast'? he asked Mick, who nodded. He turned to face Jack. 'Was it you?'

'Two of them at once? One on their own's risky, even for a full group. Besides, why do you care?' he asked.

The pair looked at each other for a moment. Then Mick said, 'One was Shell's cousin.'

That sentence sunk into Jack for a moment. Then he said, 'Shit.'

'...Yeah.'

'I don't suppose the two weren't close?'

'...No, Jack.'

He leaned back in the chair he was sitting in. 'Damn,' he said softly. Then he asked, 'What have you heard?'

'She's after whoever did it. Everyone's looking for him, big time.'

Thom repeated his question. 'So, Jack: was it you?'

He looked at them for a moment. Then he said, 'No,' and stood up. He couldn't trust them. If they got captured they might give them information. If Shell found out who killed her cousin, that person wouldn't be safe in all of Glasgow — Scotland, even. And if she caught Jack....'I have to go. I'll be in touch.' He quickly walked out before they could say anything else.

Had it been a secret government experiment run by aliens planning on creating a race of cyborg supersoliders or some such shit? Probably not. The Net abounded with theories, but Jack paid them no heed. His own theory was that it had just been another step in Evolution — one which made sense, according to the biologists who were investigating it.

The mutation was in the mitochondrial DNA — which, apparently, was only inherited down the female line (a bit like the Y-chromosome and men). How it was passed from person to person, and why it only affected women, was unknown until quite recently. Even now Jack didn't understand the specifics, but he knew it was a bacteria which was responsible — NOT some sci-fi superduper retrovirus, all of which were too small to store the geneset responsible. He knew he had it in his blood, but something on the Y-chromosome inactivated it. And he knew what it did to those who got it.

No one believed the first case: one woman against three men? It was impossible. An unseen vigilante was blamed, and the defendant was acquitted — a legal precedent which ensured that most of the new breed got off scot-free up until about 2016.

But when it happened again, and again, and again, and suddenly hundreds of women were stronger, faster, tougher than their male counterparts, the press started to ask questions. The government started to investigate, but typically poured most of their resources into adapting whatever-it-was so that they could put it into the bodies of their (predominantly male) army.

Then bodies started turning up curiously mutilated.

Then people like Jack started to fight back.

Shell came for him a month later.

He was out with a group of friends from university, other ParKours people. The Big Quake had ruined most of the city, but over the following years the new geography led to a huge rise in PK. Now it was a common thing to see someone leaping and jumping their way through the city.

Jack was at the bar when a girl approached him. He smiled at her in the mirror behind the bar, then looked away. When he looked back a moment later she was still staring at him. 'Hello, Jack,' she said.

Jack tensed up. He didn't know this woman. 'Are you from my course?' he asked, buying time, hoping she would say yes.

'No. Thom gave me your name.'

He turned to look at her, this dangerous creature standing next to him. She was about ten centimetres smaller than him, and lightly built. Shoulder-length dark-red hair framed a pale face. She was lightly-built, hardly any muscle on her at all, but Jack had found out the hard way not to be fooled by that. This girl was probably stronger now than Jack would ever be.

The bitch was still smiling at him.

He turned back to the bar and said, 'I don't know who Thom is.'

'Don't run. I have friends in the bar. We're willing to drag you out of here if we have to.'

Jack stole a glance at her, then turned to look around. She wasn't lying. Two separate tables of two girls, each stealing not-so-subtle looks at him every so often. Five against one.

He turned back. 'You really must want to talk to me.'

'Let's step outside, sweetie.'

That's what he hated the most: that contrast of danger and femininity. Many a man had been seduced, only to be found the next day with his head ripped off. He could feel his heartbeat in his chest as he paid for the drinks, asked the barman to deliver them to the table, then nonchalantly left with the girl.

'What's your name?' he asked.

'My name?' she smiled as they stepped out of the door into the Smoker's Garden. 'It's Shell.'

In the split second that it took for that to sink in, Shell had pushed Jack. He flew two or three metres before falling to the ground. But by this time PK had taken over. Jack rolled to break his fall, came up and kept running, out of the Garden and onto Gibson Street, heading for Uni.

'Shit!' he heard behind him. She hadn't been expecting that. He heard her start off in pursuit of him, and from the noise the other four girls were behind her. He ran as fast as he could.

It wasn't enough. There was no opportunity for PK in this area — in fact, it was probably the flattest bit of the city, its pockmarks and shoddy pavements in place long before the Big Quake. As he started to cross the bridge over the Kelvin she caught him, slamming into his legs and taking him roughly to the ground. The others were on the pair a moment later, grabbing his limbs and dragging him into the nearby Kelvin Park.

'Right,' Shell said once they'd laid him at the foot of a tree trunk. 'Now we're gonna have a little talk.'

'Where's Thom?' Jack spat.

'He stabbed one of my girls,' she replied. 'He's dead.' She kneeled down so she was the same height as him. 'And if you don't give me some info you're dead too.'

Jack said nothing.

'Don't look at me like that.'

Jack still said nothing.

In an instant Shell had reached forward and grabbed his neck in one hand. Jerking him forward, she spat in his face. 'Who killed my cousin?'

Jack could feel her nails, deliberately sharpened, digging into his flesh. He felt one pierce his skin as if it was wet paper,

and felt blood trickle down his neck. He felt nothing as one of the other girls kicked him in the stomach, another licking the blood from his neck as Shell screamed at him to say something, say something.

This time he did smile at them. To taunt them, to let them know they wouldn't get to him, because he thought he was a dead man. A big toothy grin that Shell tried to slap off his face.

Then their hands and feet were off him and they were running, deep into the park, faster than Jack would ever go, as red fought with blue to illuminate the area.

A minute later the police found him.

'Thom's cell's all gone,' she told him. She was standing next to the bed with some sandwiches for his lunch. 'It was on the news last night. There was a fight with some girls. NOK's investigating it.' The Non-Orthodox Killing was a unit within Strathclyde Police's CID, dealing pretty much exclusively with killings made by the girls and vigilantes. They had succeeded in bringing a few girls to justice, but they were organised and hard to capture. Once captured, it was even harder to find witnesses. The vigilante cells had few dealings with NOK, preferring to work outside the law.

'They won't find anything.' Jack coughed and sat up in bed. 'And even if they do, nothing will happen.'

She reached out and stroked Jack's hair, his cheek. 'You could have died last night.'

'I know.'

'…I want you to stop doing this once you're better.'

He didn't say anything for a moment, then said, 'I'm not going to stop.'

'Why?'

'You know why.'

'Jack, violence doesn't solve anything.'

'Bollocks. That's just bollocks they feed you to stop you from fighting. If violence didn't solve anything, why have armies? Why have the cops?'

'It just leads to people getting hurt!'

'People are hurt. Those girls are out there hurting people every day — not just men, either. Anyone who stands in their way. I'm not going to let them have the run of this fucking city. I don't care if the place is fucked, it's our city. Not theirs.'

But her eyes were already dulled. They had had this argument over a hundred times before. She put the sandwiches on the bedside table and said, 'Fine.' Lately it had become her favourite word, 'Fine,' a clear indicator that everything was not 'fine' and that they weren't going to be 'fine' anytime soon.

Standing, she left the room. Jack reached for the sandwiches, but he had lost his appetite.

Now he knew what she looked like. Tracking her was easy.

He chose his moment carefully, but even then his plan didn't have much chance of success. But truth be told, he was tired of waiting. This evening felt right.

Sitting on the platform at St Enoch, wrapped in warm clothing, Jack looked like another subway user. The beard was real, grown from the day Shell had beaten him in the park. He rested his buttocks against the wall-mounted bars that passed for seating in Glasgow's ageing underground and kept his eyes fixed on the opposite platform. Five, six trains came and went in either direction. Everyone else, of course, was intent on travelling, and didn't notice him staying put. He had also chosen a seat where he couldn't show up in camera.

At about eleven, a train pulled up. He spotted them immediately; dressed up for a good night out. It was too dangerous for cell members to go out at night; no way to defend yourself if you were drunk. It was a part of twentysomething life that had largely passed Jack by. For a moment he felt a terrible stab of jealousy. Then it was gone and he was up and moving. Suitcase by his side, he took the elevator steps two at a time and reached the top. Kneeling down, he shrugged his outer coat and garments off. He was now clothed in just a T-shirt and some lightweight trousers. He opened his suitcase to take out the fully-loaded crossbow, one of the few projectile weapons you didn't need a licence for. The goggles he put on his forehead, ready for use.

When the three girls came to the top of the opposite elevator and started to leave they didn't even notice him. He managed to get off a clear shot, a dart landing in one girl's ribs. It spun her around and she dropped soundlessly to the floor.

'Gail!' The other girl knelt down to see to her friend. Shell ducked down behind a turnstile, peeking out to see where the shot came from. Jack took a potshot at her head, made sure she had seen him, flashed her a grin, then took off back down his elevator.

He burst onto the platform, making for the Inner Circle's tunnel, heading North. A train had just gone and they were ten minutes apart at night, so he had enough time. As he entered the tunnel, not daring to look back in case he lost his balance, he slipped on the small night-vision goggles that would help him see his way. Shell's vision would be good — but it was pitch black in the subway tunnel. She'd stumble, and fall, and make her way a little slower, and hopefully by the time they came out at Buchanan Street he'd have enough of a headstart to survive.

He looked back a couple of times; each time she was further away, but not far away enough for comfort. As he neared Buchanan Street station he tore off his goggles and threw them aside, put on a burst of speed and leapt onto the platform, scaring the shit out of the few drunken revellers heading home for an early night. He ignored their cries and sped up the stairs, headed for the south exit and headed for Queen Street station.

'JACK!' he heard the scream behind him. She obviously hadn't lost his trail. But tonight that was the last thing he wanted. Turning left, he sped up Montrose Street and shouldered his way into a building Thom had used to work in. Snaking through the stairs and corridors, he made his way up the ten stories to the top. All the time Shell was on him, the sound of footsteps behind him, hard to hear over his own breathing.

Finally he reached the top, unlocking the door and inhaling a deep lungful of the night air. The door was simply for access to the roof, and was the only structure freestanding. Jack went around to the other side and waited.

He only heard the last five of her steps before she was on the roof, running to the edge, thinking he had jumped onto some surrounding structure. Quickly he dashed round to the front of the door.

Hearing the door lock, Shell turned to see Jack hurl the key over the nearest edge. For a moment she stood there silent. Then she said, 'That was really fucking stupid.'

'Oh, yeah?'

'Yeah.' She took a step closer, but stopped once she saw the knife in his hand. 'I'll just take it off you.'

He smiled, but it didn't reach his eyes. 'Try.'

She took another step towards him. 'Did you kill my cousin, Jack?'

Jack bent his knees slightly, ready to react. 'You killed my brother.'

Shell looked puzzled. 'I haven't killed anyone in years.'

'It was years ago, Shell. 2015. You got off scott-fucking-free.' Jack took a step towards her. 'I've been trying to get to you ever since.' Another step. His left hand bunched into a fist. 'Now I've got you.'

'You didn't kill Susan, did you?'

'Never even met the bitch. Now fight.'

Shell just smirked. 'What are you going to do, Jack. Are you going to kill me? I'll break your arm, take the knife off you and leave.'

'Oh, yeah? How?'

That threw her. 'Through the...'

'Door's locked.' He stepped forward again. Now they were only two metres apart. 'No other way off this roof. I chose this building specially. The only way off this roof's in the morning when someone opens it from the inside. Either they find me and your dead body or you and my dead body. If it's you dead, then fine. I'll go to jail. If it's me, you'll be arrested. And no one will believe you killed me in self-defence. Not when they find out I'm Philip's brother.'

Shell finally understood what Jack had done. 'You bastard,' she breathed. 'I'm fucked either way.'

'Five years I've waited for this,' Jack said, a broad smile on his face.

At that smile Shell leapt for him. Jack brought his knife to bear and began to fight.

He dragged himself the last few metres onto the dock, then called her name. She came running out into the night. She picked him up and carried him onto the boat, crying all the way once she saw the state of him.

'Oh, Jack...'

'I can't go to a hospital, the cops will be looking for me. I need to lie low.' He told her.

'But you've lost so much blood...'

'There's some Oral Rehydration Fluid in the cupboard, at the back in a red thermos. Go get it.'

She went to the kitchen, came back, made him drink it all. He choked down the last few sips, then said, 'Sugar. Get some coke and make it flat. Then get some new bandages.'

Getting off the roof had been a problem. He had no backup key, so had had to wait 'til morning, bleeding and broken beside Shell's dead body. To match her cousin he had decapitated her, but hadn't bothered to mutilate the body. That had never been his style, anyway. In the morning he had pounded on the door for over half an hour before a friend of Thom's had opened the door and let Jack out, quietly. The body would be discovered later, but for now Jack and Shell had effectively disappeared once they left Buchanan Street subway. After changing clothes, Jack had managed to stumble along the regenerated docklands, heading for home.

Hours later, after a dreamless sleep, Jack felt a little better. She came back into the room, bearing more bandages and flat coke. He waved them away, saying, 'I'll be okay for now.'

'We should change them before I go to work.'

'I'll be fine.'

There was a slight pause. 'What happened last night, Jack?' she asked.

'I got her.' He coughed. 'That's what happened.'

The look of shock on her face said it all. 'Alone?'

He nodded, coughed again, then sat up more. 'I got her up to a rooftop, then stabbed her. Shell's gone.'

She looked out of the window for a moment, then turned back to him. 'Does that mean you'll stop now?'

'For a while.' Jack reached over to get the coke. 'Until I'm better.' He turned to look at her. 'Don't look at me like that. You think I'm gonna stop because the one who killed Philip's dead?' She looked at the floor but didn't say anything. 'Thom's group's gone, but other cells are starting up all over. They had a headstart, but we're organising too. Soon we'll be able to fight back. Soon we'll get the city back.'

She just looked at the floor. '…I'd better go to work,' she said eventually.

'When do you start?' He asked.

'In about an hour.'

'Could you get rid of any blood on the dock, first? I probably left a trail onto the boat.'

She shook her head. 'You didn't crawl onto the boat. I carried you.'

'Sorry?'

This time she said it more quietly, but he heard it all the same. 'I carried you.'

That hung in the air for a while. Then Jack said, 'All by yourself?'

She nodded. Looked up at him, eyes wet with tears.

The shock was all over Jack's face. 'But…how lo…'

'I'd better get to work, Jack.' She stood up and made for the door. His girlfriend. His carer. The enemy. She picked up her bag and work clothes on the way. At the door she paused, and turned in the frame. 'We'll talk when I get back. I love you.' Without waiting for an answer she left.

But before she had closed the door Jack knew she'd never see him again. Knew in a few minutes he would get up, dress awkwardly, take the readypacked suitcase in the cupboard and leave. Knew it would hurt like hell, but that he'd do it anyway. She was one of them. So she wasn't safe.

Jack looked at the picture of her sitting on the chest of drawers at the foot of the bed for a very long time, before letting himself say, 'I love you too.'

JC McCrae's 'Revenge is Bitter' was the joint main prize winner in the Glasgow 2020 Story Writing Competition.

†

HAIR TODAY, GONE TOMORROW

— Laura Marney

With the most stylish salon in the most fashionable city in Europe, Sarah and Jean were at the top of their game, acknowledged leaders in the field of physical and mental wellbeing. Situated at the heart of Partick riverside in prime real estate they had the foresight to buy last century, they employed a huge staff of elite beauticians, therapists, fitness gurus, life coaches, chiropractors, nail technicians, dentists and hairdressers. Legally they could have retired years ago at seventy-five but with both of them in rude health and making more money than ever, why should they? 'No,' they often told clients, 'taking our foot of the gas is not an option.' Clients found their old fashioned way of talking cute, and everyone knew their archaic but imminently sensible motto, 'never let the grass grow under your feet.'

Sarah pushed the joystick and zoomed in on the man sitting in the waiting area. She liked to look at him from here, admiring from afar. He was a salesman, Tam McKee, and he had an appointment. Sarah had seen him every week for the last four weeks. He had begun by flirting with Sarah in a purely business-like manner but over the weeks it had gotten serious. He really fancied her, he told her so.

'Ah pure fancy you,' he'd said, 'so ah do.'

He'd said it more than once.

Sarah suspected that he was falling in love and didn't like to let the poor boy down. It wasn't fair to toy with people's emotions but she couldn't bring herself to tell him the truth. It seemed so cold. Jean and Sarah didn't do love. It was the secret of their long partnership and successful business. With plentiful supplies of Hormohorn pills they enjoyed themselves, but were faithful only to the business.

Every week Tam tried to sell Sarah a product and every week she told him she couldn't make a business decision without

Jean's approval. Could he come back next week to see them both? Every week she booked him in for a time when she knew Jean would be out. It wasn't fair but she couldn't help herself.

As he sat patiently waiting, Tam would of course know that there were cameras in all areas of the salon. It was standard practice and helped cut down the compensation claims staff and customers frequently tried to bring against them. What Tam might not know was that from here, in the control room which doubled as their panic room, with a high-spec remote x-ray facility Sarah would be able to examine what he had under his trousers. As she expected, nip and tuck. Well, she sighed, there weren't many men over fifty nowadays who hadn't had everything pulled up a bit. Or women come to that. She was no stranger to reconstruction herself. She and Jean were the sole licence holders in Europe for Natucorrect, a cutting edge procedure; these were the perks of owning an innovative business. Sarah skooshed some perfume up her skirt and prepared to welcome Tam.

Within the salon, staff were required to wear earpieces at all times. This allowed Sarah and Jean to discreetly advise and direct without disturbing the client. It also let them in on every whispered conversation: all the bitching and gossip they could not live without. Sarah now discreetly announced to all section supervisors that she was about to go into conference and was, under no circumstances, to be disturbed for the next two hours. Only very new or very naïve supervisors did not understand the euphemism. She was about to speak to reception and ask them to send Tam up when the door flew open.

Jean flounced in and threw herself into a chair.

'The bastard. George has chucked me,' she pouted.

'Go easy Jean, your next hip replacement isn't scheduled till August.'

'Did you not hear what I said? He's chucked me. He's...Get this, you'll never believe it: he's gone back to his wife! He says at his time of life he needs a friend more than a lover. At his time of life! He's only sixty three for god's sake!'

Sarah would normally have been more sympathetic but Jean's return had scuppered her own amorous plans.

'He's only a boy,' agreed Sarah, quickly organising tea while she tried to think what to do with Tam. She didn't want Jean getting her claws into him, not now she was on the market again. But when she brought Jean her mug she was alarmed to see her peruse the diary.

'Tam McKee? Who's he?'

'Oh just a salesman, I'll get rid of him and we can have our cuppa and a nice girly bitch about that git George. So, what exactly did he say?'

But it was no use.

'Oh, I don't want to go into it, it's too depressing. Men, they're all the same. Can't live with them, not allowed to stab them. Best just to move on. Wait a minute,' said Jean, returning, like a dog with a bone, to the earlier topic, 'I've seen that name in here before. Tam McKee? Has he not got some new follicle treatment?'

'Yeah, it's graft technology but it's a bit boring,' said Sarah, before trying a deflection, 'Want to go out at the week end, just me and you?'

'Graft technology?'

Jean only heard what she wanted to hear, Sarah thought sadly.

'We'll have to get in on that. There's a graft symposium coming up soon. We'll need to be up to speed. Can't let the grass grow. Let's take a look at him.'

Jean trained the waiting room camera once again on Tam, although this time without such an extreme close up.

'Mmmm,' she said, 'tasty.'

Tam did indeed look tasty, thought Sarah. Though he had been kept waiting more than fifteen minutes his body sat keen and unbeatable. His smile refused to diminish, and his blond hair glistened in the late summer light of the afternoon. He continually ruffled and smoothed down his hair as though nothing could make him happier, the whole time talking to himself.

'I don't see an earpiece. Is he using a phone?' asked Jean.

'No idea,' said Sarah, now dispirited. Jean would either offend him with her usual rudeness or charm the pants off him and steal him away. Either way Sarah had lost him.

Jean giggled, 'maybe he's got nits.'

'Probably,' said Sarah, 'he could infect the whole salon.'

'Well we could de-louse him. I'll de-trouser him any day. Let's see him in the conference suite.'

'Sorry to have kept you waiting,' said Jean, smiling broadly.

'That's alright,' said Tam cheerfully, as if he had all the time in the world. 'It's not like I'm here for a haircut. I haven't had one in two years as it goes.'

Jean shot Sarah a quizzical look. His hair was short, layered and impeccably tidy.

'What can we do for you then?'

'Actually, I'm here to change your life. Here's my card.'

Tam handed over a small white card. It was completely blank at first, and then suddenly the paper flickered into life and spoke to her.

'Tam McKee,' it said, revealing a soft-focus picture of him. The picture grinned. 'Call me anytime.'

Jean giggled with surprise. Sarah didn't. She had seen it before. It was what had first attracted her to him.

'Neat eh?' said the real Tam.

'Cool,' said Jean non-commitally, but Sarah could see she was impressed.

'Go on. Keep it.'

Sarah watched Jean carefully tuck it into her jeans pocket.

'Jean Collins and Sarah Mills,' said Sarah quickly, hoping he wouldn't let on that they'd already met.

Tam seemed to understand and gave each a polite nod, for which she was grateful.

'So what can we do for you Mr McKee?' said Jean in her I-haven't-got-time- to-stand-around-flirting-with-you voice.

Tam squared his shoulders and launched into his formal presentation. Despite herself, Sarah was keen to see this. Every week he had come, she had always managed to dissuade him from making the presentation, preferring instead their intimate chats. As there was no chance of that today, she

might as well see what he was selling.

'I'm here on behalf of Biocell Technologies,' he began. 'Don't worry, I doubt you'll have heard of us. We're a small, exclusive company…'

'I have actually,' said Jean interrupting him, 'you're speaking at the grafting symposium, aren't you? I saw your name on the programme.'

'Yes, yes I am, how amazingly observant of you! Well,' he said, starting again into sales mode, 'I'm here to offer you the opportunity of being one of the first salons to completely change the way customers have their hair styled. Let me demonstrate.' Tam now pulled out of his pocket a small sheet of paper which he carefully unfolded until it was the size of an A3 sheet.

'For thousands of years, it has been mankind's custom to style our hair with scissors. No longer. It is my pleasure to present to you,' he paused, watching and waiting for maximum effect, 'the new Biocell E-Z 2-PAY.'

The A3 sheet became a movie screen which burst into colour and celebration, culminating in a short video of handsome men and beautiful girls prancing about their lives with fabulous hair. In each shot the model's hair morphed from one minute to the next, from long and blonde to neck length brunette to black dreadlocks to auburn curls.

'How does it work I hear you ask,' said Tam.

'It's a wig' said Jean.

Tam clicked his fingers. If he was annoyed, he didn't show it.

'It's not a wig or a weave or extensions.'

'Well it must be some kind of graft.'

'Biocell E-Z 2-PAY is the ultimate in non surgical graft technology.'

'Non surgical? Then it's got to be a wig!'

Tam smiled, a knowing, rather smug smile, 'You think?'

'Well what is it then? said Jean, a hard edge creeping into her voice. She did not like to be teased, especially by salesmen. 'Is it superglued to your heid?'

'Superglued to your heeyed,' scoffed Tam, shaking his head and smiling.

Sarah noticed that he pronounced the word 'heid' with a strange accent, giving it two syllables.

'As we all know multi-resistant bacteria has become a huge problem. Surgery is no longer viable. What I'm talking about here is DNA fusion. The graft is instantaneous and permanent, that is until the DNA code is changed again. Biocell E-Z 2-PAY is the ultimate in lifestyle accessories. Get it?' smiled Tam, 'Easy toupee and easy to pay...'

'Uh huh,' said Jean, 'get on with it.'

Tam pressed on.

'With Biocell E-Z 2-PAY there's no more back breaking work for the hairdresser: just think girls, no more leaning over sinks washing clients' dirty hair. No more nicking your fingers with sharp scissors, no more standing for hours on end with your varicose veins throbbing. With Biocell E-Z 2-PAY there's no more...'

'Yeah, we get it,' said Jean, 'Biocell E-Z 2-PAY. It's a crap name.'

'Not a problem. We can change it.' said Tam quickly.

'Hmmm,' said Jean.

Sarah knew that hmmm. That hmmm meant Jean was considering buying it. If it did all he said it did, Jean would want it and she'd pay a lot for exclusive rights.

'Take out the hard work and replace it with technology,' said Tam returning to his spiel. 'Have your new hairstyle grafted on in seconds while you wait. And why restrict yourself with hair that merely looks good? Why not upgrade to our fibre-optic wireless range, where style comes fully integrated with email, internet access and the newest in hands-free digital technology? Want to make a call? Just rub your head and within seconds you're chatting to your friends without the worry of losing your phone or personal communicator. Why? Because everything's upstairs.'

Tam pointed to his hairstyle.

'On your heeyed.'

There it was again, the strange pronunciation.

'Why us?' said Jean.

'Good question. Without wanting to be obsequious, it's well known that you two are style innovators.'

Jean nodded and received the compliment with good grace.

'You know a good business opportunity when you see it. The Biocell E-Z 2-PAY, or,' he quickly added, 'whatever we end up calling it, represents genuine cost-saving efficiency. This doesn't require powering other than the energy generated by your own body heat, which means smaller energy bills and greater savings. There's no fuss with the mess and expense of chemical hair treatments like dyes and perms. Now with a simple painless injection you can choose what you like, when you like, and all without the slightest loss of style or dignity.'

With an expert bow and flourish, Tam tapped up a vein in his arm and injected himself with a small amount of lurid purple liquid. Before he had even removed the needle from his arm his beautiful soft blond hair which Sarah had dreamt of touching was falling in hunks to the floor. As it fell dark ringlet curls were sprouting from his head like time lapse photography. With his new dark hair, Sarah thought Tam looked like Heathcliffe, only more handsome.

'Perhaps you're worried that the advances we've made in follicle cell engineering will take the skill out of your profession, but please, allow me to allay your fears. The procedures involved in installing the EZ..., er, the product, are precisely those developed by the very best stylists. Hair styling is more than just cutting hair I hear you say. It's about listening to what the client wants and understanding what the client needs. It's about your artistry, your style and fashion sense. I wouldn't presume to tell you your business. Hairstyling, as it goes, is too serious a business for a computer nerd like me. With your agreement, Miss Collins, Miss Mills, I'm willing to train you and your staff to become fully conversant with fitting procedures. The future is ours.'

But Sarah wasn't listening. Miss Collins was named before Miss Mills. Tam had spent the whole time, making eye contact, making eyes, at Jean.

'Hold it a minute,' said Jean, 'Is it...'

'Safe? One hundred percent, Jean.'

Oh, Jean was it now?

'Not only has it every safety mark going, it's also,' Tam paused, 'being tested by the military. I shouldn't really be telling you this, but the news is about to break any day now. You can understand of course, the potential is immense.'

'Why here then? Why Glasgow and not somewhere more established?'

'Have you read any Rumsfeld? He was a great political philosopher. Wonderful stuff. He had this idea about knowns and unknowns. Forget Milan, forget Paris, London, New York and Tokyo, these places are so over. Everyone knows everything there is to know about them. But Glasgow? Glasgow's an unknown unknown. There are things here we don't know we don't know. You see? Glasgow's the place where things have a chance of beginning.'

He pointed to his sheet once again. In place of the immaculately nappered models there appeared an array of statistics and charts, all endlessly repeating the conclusion that Glasgow was indeed the centre of things.

'Remember the tanning-salon revolution? That started here. Back in the turn of the century, Glasgow pioneered high street tanning technology, making it cheap and easy to use. Timorous Beastie started here, now look at them. They're right up there with IKEA. Coffee tables, bedside cabinets, you name it, they do it.'

'Tam, can we offer you a cuppa?' said Jean kindly.

'Cheers Jean,' said Tam rubbing his hands in anticipation, not of the tea, but of securing a big fat contract.

This was a bad sign, thought Sarah. Jean was using the tea as a diversion. She'd catch Sarah alone and get her to agree to sign up. By the time the ink was dry, Tam would have forgotten he ever fancied her. But how could she say no?

Sarah knew that Jean was expecting her in the kitchen, but she stayed with Tam. It put off having to agree to anything.

'That was a very good pitch Tam,' she said.

'Eh? Yeah, cheers mate.'

Tam was preoccupied. Probably thinking about his lucrative contract, or worse, thinking about getting off with Jean. But there was something else.

'How's your heid?' Asked Sarah slyly.

'Sorry?'

'Your head.'

'Oh, yeah, right, me 'ead,' he replied in a strong London accent.

That was it. She had found what he had tried to hide.

'You're not from Glasgow are you Tam?'

'Er, yes, I mean aye, I mean...You won't tell her, will you?' He said, pointing his head towards the kitchen door where Jean was still dunking his tea bag. His lovely dark curls bobbed as he turned back to Sarah. 'Jean probably won't like me if she finds out I'm not a real Glaswegian.'

Sarah marvelled that he had kept it up for so long. Every week for at least an hour and a half he had kept up the pretence of a trendy Glaswegian accent. He must have taken those fashionable elocution classes. So what if he was only a Londoner? She wouldn't have cared; she would have loved him despite it. But he had lied to her. Because Jean asked the questions and was the bolshy one, he assumed Jean was the senior partner, the decision maker, and he had dropped Sarah like a scone.

'And you're not called Tam either are you?'

'Actually' he said bashfully, 'it's Tommy, but I prefer Tam. Promise you won't say anything?'

None too subtly, Jean was standing at the kitchen door gesticulating to Sarah.

'Psst!'

'Excuse me a second would you Tommy?' said Sarah making her way towards Jean.

'Well,' said Jean, 'What do you think? Are we in? Please Sadie,' she said employing the pet name she only used when she wanted something badly enough. 'I think this is a goer for us.'

Sarah thought about it. It was true that technology had been their friend. It had made them rich and successful; it had brought inventors and innovators like Tam to their door. If they took this product it would change their way of working, change their lives, but they had never been afraid of change. Technology would keep moving forward but catching a man would never change. It would always be frustrating.

Sarah was tired of man-catching, she was 83 after all. Maybe it was time to lay off the Hormohorn tablets, take a chill pill instead, take her foot off the gas.

'Okay Jean,' she said smiling, 'we're in.'

Laura Marney is the author of Only Strange People Go To Church *(2006),* Nobody Loves A Ginger Baby *(2005) and* No Wonder I Take A Drink *(2004), all published by Black Swan. A graduate of the Glasgow and Strathclyde Mlitt Creative Writing course, many of her short stories have been published in anthologies, magazines or broadcast on the radio. In her spare time she teaches creative writing and aerobics.* 'Hair Today, Gone Tomorrow' *was written in response to a Glasgow 2020 event involving hairdressers.*

†

THE PROG ROCK CAFÉ

— Alan Bissett

'Well, Chantelle, you can choose to believe four and a half billion Christians, Jews, Sikhs, Hindus and Muslims, or you can believe the theory of one man. And remember, Chantelle, it's called the theory of evolution.'

'That's what she told you?' said Flo, her joints creaking as she reached to adjust the tins of plaster mix, 'I mean, I knew they were bringing that stuff back in, but I didn't realise it was getting so bad. What school are you at?'

'The Arnold Clark School.'

'Used to be Hillhead Academy?'

Chantelle nodded and turned the pricing gun over in her hands. She was proud of her hands, Flo could see. Her nails were painted brilliant black and she had henna tattoos, as well as four elaborate rings which she wore at all times, even after management had warned her they were inappropriate. This was the sole advantage of the new labour laws: though firms were obliged to hire youths and the elderly, they couldn't fire them unless for gross misconduct. The wages were pathetic, but they couldn't be sacked, which led to the oldest and youngest of the workforce seeking whichever little rebellions they could get away with. Chantelle's was coming to work in her punk gear. Flo's was, quite frankly, farting in front of customers. She could see them turn their heads sharply when they noticed the noise or smell, and she'd come over all defeated and sigh, 'It's my bowels, dear. Not what they used to be.' Chantelle would suppress a smirk and they'd laugh about it in the canteen at tea-breaks. This was another unexpected benefit of the laws. When Flo had been young — in the heady Sixties and early Seventies — it was a fashion crime to be seen consorting with the aged, those relics from World War II, that dusty, drab era before the psychedelic revolution. But now, with the old and the young forced into tabards and chucked together into whatever menial corners could be found, they'd united against the new enemy: these smug, careerist fuckwits in-between, who'd barely deign to speak to them in the canteen, and who — since they themselves were eminently disposable — quietly resented the things Flo and Chantelle could get away with.

They'd given Flo the decorative mouldings section, mainly because coving wasn't heavy to lift, but also because she'd been a set designer for radical theatre groups back in the Seventies, which had impressed them in the interview. Besides, she'd been pasting, painting or rearranging since she and Allen had moved into their first flat in '67. She remembered it well. It was the year Sgt Pepper and Piper at the Gates of Dawn had come out. She still saw Allen's excitement about bringing them home into the huge collection of LPs which he'd already amassed and which would eventually evolve, once she'd insisted he get rid of some of it (did he really need an LP, eight-track and quadrophonic mix of Tubular Bells?) into the beginnings of the Prog Rock Café. Flo knew plenty of people who'd been unlucky with the jobs they'd found though. Her friend Dilys was in McDonald's, which was fast, constant work for a seventy-year-old, and Allen, she was slowly realising, was going to have to keep the Café open until the day he died. Unless it shut down first. Which seemed more likely.

'It's so unfair,' said Chantelle, 'Why do we have to work, just to help save money for some stupid war that's been going on for, like, 15 years? You'd think they'd realise by now they can't win it.'

'In the old days,' said Flo, disliking, even as she said, the feel of the cliché in her mouth, 'I'd have a pension and you'd have a grant. Good ones too.'

'My Dad told me that,' said Chantelle, 'But he also says why should his taxes pay for hand-outs to folk that are capable of working, when the country needs money to fight the enemy?'

'Hm,' said Flo.

'I hate this stupid job.' Chantelle threw the pricing gun into a box of packaging and scowled at a customer.

'At least you don't have to do it for the rest of your life,' said Flo. 'Unlike me. I mean, you're still young. What do you really want to do?'

'I want to make a go of it with the band.'

'Oh yes. What are they called again?'

'Chicks With Blades.'

'And what kind of music is, um, "Chicks With Blades"?'

'Punk,' smirked Chantelle, 'It's loud and it's fast. We even got banned from our school talent show. Said we were too extreme.'

'They seem to say that about a lot of things.'

'Contest was won by a girl doing songs from the fucking Sound of Music.'

Flo shook her head. She remembered her own mother playing her The Sound of Music LP when she was in her teens, just as Flo was getting into The Rolling Stones and The Who. 'Wholesome material,' her mother had said, dropping the needle into the groove delicately, 'Not like your nasty Mick Jaguar. Don't know how you can listen to that rubbish, Florence.' Fifty-five years on and some things really hadn't changed, Flo reflected. But others certainly had. To think that she used to be a socialist, that her husband's nickname had actually been Red Allen. This was back in the Sixties, Seventies and Eighties, when revolution still seemed possible, indeed, imminent, when Glasgow was still alive with fight and fury and radicalism. Now there was an awareness, behind the banter with Chantelle, behind the sniggered nicknames they'd assign to their least-favourite fuckwits, behind every secret smirk each time Flo farted, that even Chantelle would eventually become one of them. It was inevitable. She'd soon realise she needed a career, that she would have to 'stick in' and 'play the game' and start 'looking out for herself'. And Flo couldn't blame her. So this snotty little punk kid with all her spirit and defiance would soon be lost into the guts of the machine like everyone else.

Flo racked more tins of plaster mix, pausing to clutch at her back, while Chantelle picked up the pricing gun and starting firing at an imaginary enemy.

Another couple came in and glanced

round for a table, before choosing the one shaped like a glass prism. Flo saw Allen hold back, smiling, while they played with the Van Der Graaf Generator and giggled. After two minutes of Yes's 'Tales From a Topographic Ocean' and a quick scan of the menu, however, they looked at each other then stood and left, just a few seconds before Allen could reach their table, notepad out, ready to take their order. He slumped back down next to Flo. 'They didn't even get the chance to try out the Prawn Salad Surgery.'

'Or the…' Flo picked up the menu, '… Roast Lamb Lies Down on Broadway.'

Allen shook his head. 'It's not looking good, you know.'

Flo nodded. 'I know.'

'We need something to remind people we're still here. An event. Something to bring the kids back in.'

'The kids', Flo wanted to remind him, hadn't been 'in' since the dawn of punk in '77, when hanging round a café which played nothing but prog rock had become the epitome of uncool. The place had had enough of a cult reputation, though, enough of a name in the guidebooks, to see it through the leanest of times. It had all picked up again in the noughties, when prog had had something of a rehabilitation and Radiohead-loving indie kids had discovered Allen's place. But fashion had taken its usual about-face, and now, beyond the diminishing trickle of stoners, hippies and rockers, who liked the cheap food, the ancient copies of Mojo, or an in-depth chat with Allen about Peter Gabriel, it was starting to look bleak. He'd even placed his vast and beloved music collection on eBay, though it didn't really appeal to anyone who couldn't tell the difference between Camel, Kansas and Porcupine Tree.

'Don't worry,' said Flo, 'It'll pick up.'

'And if it doesn't?'

'I can always do more shifts in B&Q.'

'Hm,' he said, 'Looks like I'll have to as well.'

The door opened and they both looked up. It was Chantelle. She strode towards their table and slung her bag onto a seat. 'I've been suspended from school,' she announced, grinning.

'You're joking,' said Flo, 'What for?'

'They told me to do the Bible reading at assembly and I read from The Origin of Species instead.'

Allen laughed. 'Good girl!'

'What are you going to do?' said Flo.

Chantelle reached for a Robert Fripp Chip.

'Well, I could go full-time at B&Q for a couple of weeks. But maybe I should just concentrate on the band, get some gigs going.'

'Chicks With Blades,' Flo said to Allen.

'Sounds relaxing,' frowned Allen and tapped the table. 'Listen, I've a room in the back of the café. I'm thinking about putting bands on again. We did it in the Seventies. Acoustic sets.'

'Get anybody famous?'

'Only the Sandy Denny and the Kevin Ayers.'

Chantelle blinked.

'Never mind,' said Allen, 'Anyway. You want to play?'

'No offence, Mr Miller,' said Chantelle, 'But I don't really think we're the right band for this kind of place.'

'What do you mean?'

'Well look around. I don't know who the people are in these pictures, but one of them's dressed as a fox, one of them's playing the flute, and one of them's singing from behind a giant wall!'

'Oh c'mon,' said Allen, 'Even you must have heard of Pink Floyd?'

'God,' said Chantelle, 'The name says it all! Not exactly going to be music with an edge, is it?'

'You'd be surprised.'

Chantelle made her hands into fists. Her henna tattoos stretched across her skin. 'Not as if you can jump up and down and release some frustration to it. Progressive rock?'

'Point is it's progressive,' said Flo. She didn't even like prog rock, but was irritated by Chantelle's scattergun cynicism. 'Unlike the rubbish you're being taught in schools these days.'

'Well I think anger is a much better way of bucking the system than 20-minute symphonies with whale noises in the middle.'

Allen thought for a second then went to his CD player. Chantelle watched him fiddling with it. 'Wow,' she whispered to Flo, 'He still has CDs?'

'Dear,' Flo said, 'He still has vinyl.'

'What's vinyl?'

A track tore from the stereo, making both of them flinch: someone screamed, a rhythm guitar chugged, and a voice intoned: 'We don't need no education...We don't need no thought control.'

Chantelle sat back in her seat and tutted. Allen crossed his arms and looked at her.

'No dark sarcasm in the classroom... Teacher leave them kids alone.'

'You want to borrow it?' said Allen.

'You want to borrow a Chicks With Blades demo?'

'Fine,' smirked Allen, 'The Floyd probably invented you anyway.'

'The Floyd.' Chantelle shook her head. 'God!'

Flo was there when Allen received the letter informing him of the rise in rent. He took one glance at it then placed it down on the phone table, and passed Flo in the hall without even looking at her. 'Commensurate with market prices,' was how they'd put it. Flo didn't even need to ask if he could afford to renew the lease this time. He went straight into his 'music suite' — a cramped boxroom crowded with CDs, LPs, and a single armchair — and soon she heard the tinny sound of In The Court of the Crimson King trickle from his gigantic headphones. Flo closed the door, and left him to his private universe of dancing puppets and fire witches.

The next evening Chantelle was back into the Café, with Allen's copy of The Wall and a bright, excited look in her eyes. She'd had to fish her Dad's old CD player out of the attic to play it on, but play it she had. And she seemed eager to speak to Allen about it.

'Great, isn't it?' Allen beamed.

'Are you joking?' Chantelle asked, 'It's terrible! Bombastic and dull and self-indulgent. But the lyrics. Listen to this: 'Did did did you see the frightened ones? / Did did did you hear the falling bombs / Did did did you ever wonder why we had to run for shelter / With the promise of a brave new world unfurled beneath the clear blue sky?' I thought prog was supposed to be about hobbits and space and stuff?'

Allen shrugged and said, 'some of it is,' then Flo watched as he and Chantelle wound themselves further around the themes of the album — 'they built a huge wall between themselves and the audience, y'know, to represent alienation. Then at the end of the show they brought it crashing down' — and found herself drifting further from the heat and light Chantelle and Allen were generating, as though they were seated round a camp-fire and no-one had noticed her silently slipping into the darkness. When she went upstairs to bed, her 'goodnight' unanswered, they were still talking, and she could hear the intonation of their excited voices like rubber balls against the underside of the floor.

When she woke next morning Allen was bringing her breakfast in bed, a pot of tea steaming and the smell of bacon filling the room. Flo stretched and cracked. 'What's this in aid of?' she yawned.

Allen was grinning. He rested the tray on her lap and poured a mug of tea. 'Chantelle's had a terrific idea,' he said. 'She says she's had it with that school, and I don't blame her. She's 17 anyway and doesn't have to go back if she doesn't want to.'

'So what's her idea?'

Allen threw open the curtains. Flo blinked against the blaze of light. 'How many people do you think we could fit in the street out there?'

'Allen, what? I don't know.'

'How wide do you think it is?'

'I've no idea. What's the...'

'The Wall,' he said, making a widescreen image with his hands, like a movie producer asking someone to picture the scene. Flo hadn't seen him this animated in years. 'Sponsored by the Prog Rock Café. Performed by Chicks With Blades.'

'Chicks With Blades?' stammered Flo, 'But they don't sound a thing like Pink Floyd.'

'Exactly!' he said, 'We'll draw in the

punks and the hippies. Open air gig. Build a huge wall across the street...' He clicked his fingers. 'We'll call it Wall Street!'

'Wall Street?' said Flo, flummoxed, 'Allen, have you thought about the logistics of this? How much it's going to cost? How long it's going to take to prepare?'

'Ach away,' said Allen, waving his hand.

'We just don't have that kind of cash or time to spare. And you're too old for something like this anyway.'

He turned towards the window, and before he did so she saw doubt flash for a second in his eyes, and felt a quaver of guilt for putting it there.

'Look,' said Flo, running her hands through her hair, 'I can understand where this is coming from. She's young. The young are exciting. And she's very pretty.'

Allen had been staring into the street at his vast, imagined stage set, but now turned to look at her. 'What are you implying, Flo?'

'Nothing,' said Flo, 'I'm just saying that she's a good-looking girl, and the attention she's showing you must be quite...flattering. But don't run away with yourself, Allen, eh?'

Allen crossed the room and sat down on the edge of the bed. The flicker of excitement had been extinguished from his eyes. He spoke low and clear. 'Florence Miller, are you suggesting that I'm trying to get into that girl's pants?'

'No,' she scoffed, 'Of course not!'

'Because she's 52 years younger than me, Flo. Remember that.'

Flo placed her hand onto Allen's, felt the skin, papery, the gnarled bone beneath. She suddenly felt sad. For him, for her, for Chantelle, for the hopeless, hare-brained scheme they'd concocted together, for everything, which, it seemed to her, had worsened with each passing year since the glittering, optimistic days of the Sixties. 'I know that, darling,' she said, 'I wasn't implying anything.'

'Good,' he said, and stood, 'Then you won't mind if we go ahead.'

Flo could only sit back and watch, half in despair, half in wonder, as Allen started to tumble back through the years, shedding weariness as he went, phoning round trying to organise the impossible. The Prog Rock Café had, it seemed, still enough of a place in the hearts of the long-haired and the tie-dyed, just that most of them were too old or too stoned to be much help. They'd turn up and Allen would stand with them out in the street, pointing here, sweeping his hand there, and they'd nod eagerly, then Flo would see them ask Allen questions. Allen would shake his head, and they'd amble off, then he'd come back inside, sit down in the booth with her and say, 'They wanted to know where they could get some weed.'

Chantelle's friends proved a bit more helpful. She'd bring the band, and their hordes of 12 year-old admirers, round to the Café and rehearse in short, alarming blasts in the un-soundproofed room through the back. The amount of customers this scared away was offset, though, by the ravenous, mascara-ed teenies that followed Chicks With Blades, all of whom had developed a liking for Rushburgers and Tangerine Dream Ice-Cream. The music seemed to be falling into place. Even a MySpace-prompted crowd seemed a formality. It was the staging that was proving most difficult. Allen and Chantelle would sit in the Café after it had been locked, staring at drawings of a styrofoam wall dominating the street and wondering where the hell they were going to get the materials and how they were going to build the damn thing.

Flo would approach with a tray of tea, which she'd set down on the table. They'd move the plans then grunt, while she simply hovered there.

'...if we can get people to be building it while we play the first half of the set...'

'But what's going to keep it up? How are the bricks going to fit together?'

Flo peered over their shoulders. They ignored her.

The further into their project they went, the less Flo saw of either of them. So she simply spent her spare time in B&Q, lifting, carrying, sweeping, arranging, farting.

Management had asked everyone in for an emergency staff meeting. People were crowded into the hot, fussy canteen, swapping rumours about the announcement. Flo didn't care what it was. Her hip still ached. She'd reached to hang a dado rail and slipped off the step-ladder and fallen, and it had taken minutes for her to get back up, her hip firing painful warnings.

She would be seventy in a couple of months' time.

She wanted her husband and her friend back. Her mind was engaged with what they could be doing right then: his hand moving towards hers over the plans, the feel of her young skin. His aged fingers drawing down her bra-strap, their lips meeting...

A suited figure from management called for order. Flo turned his way but she was barely listening. She could feel her heart, empty and echoing. She could feel her bones tremble. She placed her head in her hands.

It was something about 'having to be competitive'. It was something about 'profits being down'. It was something about streamlining the middle layer of workers' and bringing in more 'diverse' labour.

Somebody near Flo stood up and shouted, 'That's a lot of crap! You're just talking about hiring more young and old people cos they'll work for less!' There were roars of agreement. The suit held up his hands and shook his head. Flo managed to hear the words 'voluntary redundancies' before the images in her head of Allen and Chantelle collided together, passionate and seething, and she was stumbling for the door, hand outstretched, head on fire.

On the morning of the gig, the clouds were low and dark. Flo feared it might rain. Allen seemed as removed from her as usual, calling the papers to make sure they were coming to cover it, calling friends and customers from years back to remind them about the show. Chantelle was in the back room with Chicks With Blades, thrashing out a last minute rehearsal. Flo stood in the street outside the Prog Rock Café, alone, feeling the wind whip against her face. Whenever she tried to approach either of them they'd stop, before she could even tell them anything, and say, 'You alright, Flo? You want anything. You just take it easy, make sure you've got yourself a good view

for the gig.' Like she was an old person.

She was an old person.

By five a decent-sized crowd had gathered. Not as many as they were hoping for, but a good couple of hundred anyway. Flo floated around behind the stage while Chantelle and the Chicks did their make-up — elaborate black scars across their faces. Allen was taking ticket money.

'You okay?' said Flo, to a visibly harrassed Chantelle.

'Yes,' she said, 'No,' she said, 'Well. I think this would have been a much better gig if we'd actually managed the stage set we wanted, with the wall and everything.'

Flo was silent.

'What?' said Chantelle.

'Nothing,' said Flo, and sipped her tea. It was all she'd become good for recently, sipping tea and keeping out of the way.

'Look,' sighed Chantelle, 'I'm really sorry I've been monopolising so much of Allen's time.'

Flo shrugged.

'I know you haven't seen either of us for weeks, but...' She searched around for words. 'This has been so important to both of us. It could really get my band off the ground, and bring some punters back into the Café.'

'Yes,' Flo said.

'We're still friends aren't we?' said Chantelle.

'Still friends,' said Flo.

Chantelle hugged her, leather creaking between them. 'Okay,' said Chantelle, sweeping her black hair back from her white face, 'Wish me luck.'

Flo murmured something she hoped was positive.

Flo went out and took her place next to Allen at the side of the stage. They smiled at each other, but something had changed between them. Allen had that same thrilled look in his eyes he used to get whenever he'd brought home another LP way back when they'd first moved in — Frank Zappa's Hot Rats, or the new Fairport Convention — and Flo for her part, felt older, even older than her years. If she herself hadn't had so much work in B&Q, she'd probably have slipped away entirely, through the gap between the two of them, and the memories of the bad times which had appeared again like cracks across the years.

When Chantelle took the stage, Allen couldn't take his eyes off her. When she slashed out the chords of 'Another Brick in the Wall' and started leading the crowd on a chant of 'Hey! Teacher! Leave them kids alone!' he began clapping, even whooping. Flo could see the dark rebellion in Chantelle glitter, the way it infected the pogo-ing crowd. There was something there. Something she hadn't seen in a crowd since the early days of the war protests, before it had all fizzled out and people had resigned themselves to getting by and getting on. Now it was her who didn't care. Allen could have this little fantasy crush. He'd need something to comfort him when all this was over, because Flo really didn't think she herself would be around much longer.

When the numbers started to swell at the back of the crowd, people attracted by the sound and energy, Allen's eyebrows raised, then when the guys from B&Q started appearing onstage with huge styrofoam bricks, which they started to lay in accordance with the set design Flo had given them, he turned to her, staring.

'Did you know anything about this?'

She nodded. 'It's funny the materials that people sacked by a DIY firm can, uh, "stumble across".'

He was looking at her, dumbstruck, with an expression part-incomprehension, part-awe. And so did Chantelle every so often, onstage, as the bricks slowly started to rise around her, so that by the finale of the show the wall was complete, stretching right across the street, the audience cheering and whistling as Chantelle was obscured from sight.

Alan Bissett is the author of two novels: The Incredible Adam Spark (Headline Review, 2005) and Boyracers (Polygon, 2001). In 2000 he was shortlisted for the Macallan/ Scotland on Sunday short story prize. He is currently a tutor on the MPhil in Creative Writing at University of Glasgow. 'The Prog Rock Café' was written in response to a Glasgow 2020 event with people who work and are passionate about arts and culture.

†

PART 5

DESIGN CODE FOR MASS IMAGINA-TION

TRUSTED
RELATIONSHIPS

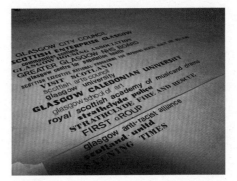

DISRUPTIVE SPACES

STARTING WITH PEOPLE

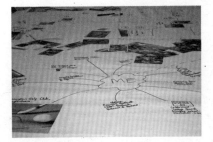

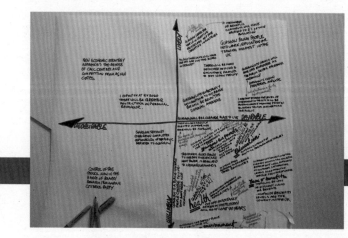

CREATING SCENARIOES FOR THE FUTURE

STORY CREATION

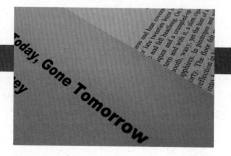

CONTINUING
THE STORY

Wishes for Glasgow

"Glasgow will be a clean city, free from pollution, litter, racism, sectarianism, violence and crime"

Submitted by: from The Big Dream on 30/08/2006. Average score: 3.90 after 29 votes.

Give this Wish a Rating:

STORYTELLING
TO ACTION

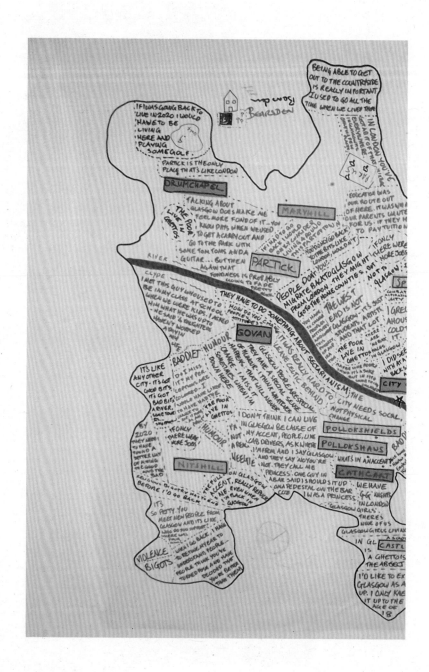

—158—

Glasgow 2020 searched for the unofficial stories of the city's future: the stories that live outside institutions, strategy documents and media rhetoric; shared stories that weave their way in and out of different age groups, backgrounds and cultures; stories which resonate and are inspired by people's everyday lives and aspirations. These are stories that had to come from the public imagination.

A search for new stories for the future of a city demands a new approach. It requires working at different scales across the city, with established communities and emerging ones, in the spaces between large institutions, community groups and individuals. It means working firmly in the public arena but also maintaining a level of personal intimacy.

The following design principles share the methodology of the project and are offered as a source book for other neighbourhoods, towns and cities which are interested in developing an independent, reflective public space and process for people to imagine the future together.

NETWORK LOGIC. The critical element in a citywide process of mass imagination is people. Forging wide and diverse networks and partnerships are vital in securing awareness, credibility and trust. Instead of expecting people to automatically participate, preparatory and ongoing work needs to be done with and through trusted intermediaries and relationships to reach and invite people and communities to take part.

In Glasgow 2020, the core project team drew on four organisations and their networks: Demos (a think tank), Oyster Arts (an arts organisation), 101 Dimensions (organisational change facilitators) and Infinite Eye (web developers and designers). All the significant public sector agencies in the city supported Glasgow 2020, which worked through their networks. In addition, the team worked with a wider and looser network of collaborators including community and youth groups, hair salons, cafés, and artists. The result was a project that was able to connect with the formal Glasgow of council officers and quango chief executives, and people in galleries and libraries, in tower blocks and outlying schemes, on public transport, in cafés and bars, and in the Gambia, Helsinki, Gothenburg and Stockholm.

IMAGINATION
NOT CONSULTATION. The last decade has seen
a greater emphasis on community involvement in decision-making in an effort to make a break from some of the socially divisive urban policies of the 1980s and 1990s. However, consultation has often proved frustrating in practice with — at best — a great deal of ambiguity about how much real power or freedom communities have to influence decisions. Indeed many consultations have left people and communities feeling that options have been closed down long before any public discussions begin.

In contrast mass imagination seeks to open all discussion and topics up. By not pre-programming questions or answers, the process gives voice and space to people's everyday concerns and enables people to connect together different futures in ways that makes sense to them. Nor do people feel as if they are being tested or hemmed in by trying to second-guess what the 'right answer' might be. As such the issues and perspectives raised have an authenticity.

Glasgow 2020 used two main tools to help open the conversation up: story and culture. Story because it is the natural way that people communicate and understand the world around them. Culture because increasingly culture is proving a far more effective way to tackle collective questions than our current political or policy language. There were 38 events, none of which had a pre-set agenda other than to explore Glasgow's future. Tools such as storytelling, role-playing, drawing and animation were used to facilitate the discussions.

Rather than using abstract trends or predictions people built up their pictures and route maps for the future through developing characters and thinking about how real people would live in the scenarios they created. When people imagined the future at the level of the person, a duty of care quickly developed, almost a need to find a happy ending even if their personal starting point for imagining the future was grim. The characters people chose and nurtured were often those deemed outside the mainstream — the old, the young, the new immigrant, the artist. This helped test the futures created and see if they really worked for a diverse range of people. People often showed an innate curiosity and inventiveness for the kind of life beyond their own direct experience.

DIFFERENT STROKES FOR DIFFERENT FOLK.

People approach the future from very different starting points, with a real mix of motivations, needs and resources which help frame their expectations, desire and ability to engage. Some people might not be comfortable or able to read and write, some have never used a computer before, others don't read newspapers, or don't speak English. There need to be many different access routes and invitations into public imagination.

One of the most accessible elements in Glasgow 2020 was the wish campaign inviting people to make a wish for the kind of city they wanted in 2020. Freepost postcards were distributed in public buildings around the city, celebrities cast their wishes in a full-page splash in the local paper, and a giant wishbook toured schools, offices and public buildings collecting wishes. People could also submit their wish on the website, where they could be viewed and rated by other visitors.

Finally, all the six-year-olds in Glasgow (who will turn 21 in 2020) were written to and invited to make a wish — over 1000 of them did so.

People could get more deeply involved in the project by coming to the public events, organising their own 2020 event, or submitting a story or poem in a city-wide short story competition.

USING DISRUPTIVE SPACES AND EVERYDAY SPACES.

Glasgow 2020 was an independent project, which created a reflective, experimental thinking space for the city, its people and its institutions alike. Creating a different mental map of a city through a process of mass imagination requires taking the conversation beyond the standard policy and political landscape of committee rooms and community halls. The project aspired to work in what Hajer and Reijndorp have called 'the new public domain':

> ' The new public domain appears at the usual places in the city, but often develops in and around the in-between spaces… in surroundings that belong to different social, economic and cultural landscapes — these are border crossings, places where the different worlds of the inhabitants of the urban field touch each other.'[104]

Glasgow 2020 occupied this space in two ways. First, it took discussions about the future of the city into the everyday public spaces of the city — into hair salons, cafés, libraries and museums in order to tap into the bottom-up intelligence of the city. And also to signal that the shared future of Glasgow was not a closed game to be played in smoke-filled rooms by experts and grandees, but instead a tangibly public enterprise.

Second, the project set up a series of 'disruptive spaces'. These experimental events helped to open up different perspectives and conversations as the unusual setting encouraged people to be more open. These disruptive events included turning a boat into a floating office for a day; taking over trains between Glasgow and Edinburgh for two days; installing three cargo cabins filled with art in different neighbourhoods across the city; and *The Big Dream,* an interactive futures festival at the Kelvingrove Art Gallery and Museum.

The aim with all the events was to create a 'trading zone' where different people could come together as equals and exchange different experiences, beliefs and hopes about the future. Harvard Professor Peter Galison coined the trading zone term to describe places that are 'partly symbolic and partly spatial — at which the local coordination between beliefs and actions takes place'.[105]

AN OPEN TOOL BOX. Mass imagination is not something to be defensively guarded. It is a public good: the more open it is and the more it is given away, the stronger it becomes. The process of imagining the future cannot be totally owned by the organisation instigating it. It needs to be something that different people and organisations can pick up and run with.

Glasgow 2020 publicised the fact that it was

ready to support any individuals or organisations that were interested in creating their own Glasgow 2020 event. A range of events happened with this support, including a series of discussions in a women's library, a visioning process by the Port of Glasgow community, and a neighbourhood church's summer school, which made a giant 3D model of the city as its creators imagined it would look in 2020.

THE FREEDOM OF INFORMATION.

Public imagination is not a process that can or should have one narrator or interpreter. The role of the Glasgow 2020 team was to act as facilitators and animators, helping people to understand, articulate and exchange their own views and hopes for the future of Glasgow. It was important that the process was transparent and stories and ideas were able to circulate, helping prompt further reflection and development of new ideas.

Glasgow 2020 encouraged three different spheres of conversation to make the process as inclusive and far-reaching as possible. First, the public sphere, which comprised the make-a-wish campaign; the short story writing competitions; the media partnership with, and coverage in, the *Evening Times*; and a dedicated Glasgow 2020 website.[106] Second, the community sphere, which covered a range of events with specific geographic, identity and interest groups. And third, the official sphere comprising events and discussions with city institutions and public organisations.

The circulation of ideas between these three spheres was encouraged. So for example, using techniques derived from grounded theory,[107]

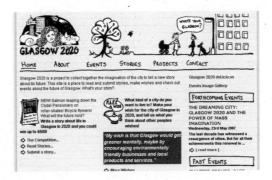

where data is developed experientially through the
gathering of material and the shaping of patterns,
wishes and elements of stories submitted were
used as starting points for discussions in workshops.
These workshops produced stories, which in turn were
given to authors who developed particular characters
and storylines into complete stories. These stories were
then distilled into seven emerging storylines for the future
(see part 7), which were publicly tested and refined at
the futures festival at the Kelvingrove to which over
700 people came.

The combination of these six principles adds up
to a project that is partly a campaign (as it seeks to enlist
people in futures thinking and to encourage them to use
their voices as citizens), partly a public culture project
(as it engages people's imagination) and partly
a piece of policy research (as it generates learning
for the development of urban policy and practice in
an inclusive way).

The pages at the start of this section illustrate
how these principals translated into the Glasgow 2020
project process.

PART

6

A CITY OF
IMAGINA -
TION

' Scotland's post-industrial hangover is finally over. There is much talk of the future...'
— Croft No. 5, *Talk of the Future* [108]

There are essentially two ways that are helpful in structuring how we think about the future: what is possible and what is desirable. In other words, what could happen and what would people like to happen. The 2020 Project sought to take these two questions out of the boardroom, university department, and futurologist's Powerpoint, and place them firmly in the public realm. This chapter shares people's responses that came in the form of: • wishes
• questionnaire responses
• group discussions

WHAT'S IN A WISH?

' I'll bet a lot of you folks don't believe that, about a wish coming true, do ya? We'll I didn't either. Course, I'm just a cricket, but lemme tell you what made me change my mind. You see, the most fantastic, magical things can happen, and it all starts with a wish! '
— Jiminy Cricket

' Wishes are like dreams — always dream them two sizes too big so that you can grow into them.'
— Glasgow Book of Wishes

What kind of city do people want to live in come 2020? Instead of clipboards armed with a list of questions and boxes to be ticked, the people of Glasgow were invited to indulge in some wishful thinking. A giant wish book toured offices and public buildings, freepost wishcards were dropped in bars, libraries and community centres, and a website invited people to make a wish themselves and to rank other people's wishes. Why wishes? There is something about the child-like naïvety and idealism of wishes, their simplicity and hope. This was not a consultation exercise; there were no right or wrong answers, and no limits to the dreaming.

So what patterns emerge from the total of well over 2000 wishes that were collected?

> ' I wish for a fast car, a nice lady, and loadsa money.'
> ' I wish I was taller.'
> ' I wish I was smaller.'
> ' I wish the world was made of chocolate.'
> ' I wish I was spiderman.'
> ' I wish we have flying buses.'
> ' I wish we had robot teachers.'
> ' I wish I win the lotto jackpot.'

Beneath the Jetsons-style futures, dreams of personal riches, and the odd fantastic fantasy, seven clear clusters of wishes emerged, which together powerfully map out people's shared priorities for what kind of Glasgow people want to live in. In a number of cases, involvement in the process itself appears to spark off some potential positive personal actions that could have an impact on the city, as people use their wishes to make individual statements about their own behaviours, clearly recognising that each person affects those around them.

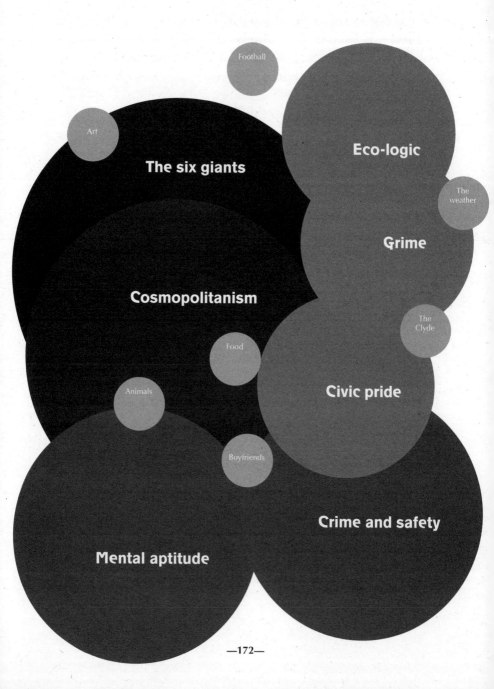

The six giants:
In 1942 the great social economist Beveridge identified
five evils for society to conquer: Want, Disease,
Ignorance, Squalor and Idleness, and with them
laid the groundwork for the birth of the welfare
state. More than 60 years on the people of Glasgow
identify their own giants they wish to see the end of,
which reflect something of Beveridge's spirit: poverty,
bad housing, inequality, poor health, poor education
and unemployment.

' Help the poor people, give them money, new homes, more
clothes and better clothes.'

' I want poor people to live in peace and have enough money
to eat and live happily.'

' Renting a house will not be seen as a second class option,
nor an option for a poor living situation, but will allow the
possibility of a quality home in a healthy environment.'

' I wish to see a Glasgow with fresh air, better health and
much less social and economic inequality.'

' A city with genuine social equality and prospects. I hate that
life expectancy is so different between different areas.'

' A Glasgow that has successfully turned around its appalling
education record, and rescued future generations.'

Cosmopolitanism:

This cluster is a mix of wishes to resolve long-borne Glasgow problems of sectarianism, desires for increased tolerance, integration, and wishes for the city to be open and welcoming to difference and newcomers:

> ' I hope we are all embracing different cultures and social backgrounds, accepting people for who they are and realise we all have a part to play to make Glasgow great.'

> ' I will contribute more actively to the local community and that more festivals bring cultures of Glasgow together and more frequently.'

> ' I wish that Glasgow would become a vibrant and more tolerant society. For all creativity to be promoted.'

> ' For a city free from the evils of racism and sectarianism, where everyone that lives and works here treats all others with dignity and respect. No to racism, bigotry, fascism and nationalism!'

> ' I wish in 2020 that people see Glasgow for the fabulous and diverse city that it really is. I hope we are all embracing different cultures and social backgrounds, accepting people for who they are and realise we all have a part to play to make Glasgow great. I hope we are all proud to call ourselves Glaswegians.'

Mental aptitude:

This cluster comprises wishes that people possess the right mental attitude and skills to prosper in 2020. The aptitudes range from self-confidence and having a positive outlook to compassion and friendliness towards others:

' I wish that everybody was nice to each other.'

' I wish that people in Glasgow will be more positive and have more confidence in their abilities.'

' I wish that the youth of Glasgow to be given a belief in their abilities and the courage and self confidence to fulfil their dreams and aspirations.'

' I wish that Glaswegians were more confident and comfortable giving and receiving praise.'

' I wish that Glasgow come to terms with its own contradictions — contradictions of race, religion, wealth... and its own contradiction as the poor man of Europe. It's the richest city I've ever known.'

Crime and safety:
Wishes for an end to crime, violence and substance abuse are underscored by a hope for a broad sense of safety to enable people to enjoy the freedom of the city:

' I wish that in the near future that night-time in Glasgow became a safe and quiet time so that I and all could sleep well at night.'

' An old lady could walk safely down the street carrying a bag of gold!'

' I wish that shops that sell knives would sell something else.'

' I wish that there were no robbers in Glasgow.'
' That I can go anywhere in the city at the weekend and not
be afraid of being harassed or attacked and can get home
quickly and safely when I want.'

Civic pride:

This cluster of wishes carries an internal and external
dimension. Internally, there are hopes that people have
more pride in their city and recognise its special qualities
and more actively contribute to creating and maintaining
them. Externally, there are hopes that Glasgow is
recognised by other people and places as a great city:

' I wish Glaswegians were proud of their city as we all should
be and that the thriving culture and idiosyncrasies that make

Glasgow what it is go from strength to strength.'

' My wish is for Glasgow to continue being a great city and
not to submerge its identity by trying to be like every other
city — we are different. '

' My wish is that I am still around to enjoy the wit and humour
of my fellow Glaswegians! '

' I wish that people outside of Glasgow knew what a great city
it is, and that it lost its reputation as a rough city as it's no
worse than anywhere else. '

' I wish like myself all Glaswegians would take pride in
their city. Get more involved in what's going on and try
to help in projects like cleaning up the Clyde and better
neighbourhood schemes. Come on, make Glasgow
even better!!!'

Grime:
Alongside the more noble Six Giants run five grubbier
scourges that people would like to imagine a future
without — litter, gum, graffiti, spitting and dog dirt:

' I wish the powers-that-be would do something about dog
owners allowing their dogs to foul up pavement, and spitting
on streets. It is worse than smokers putting fag butts on the
road, and they are being fined for this.'

' My wish is that there would be no litter or graffiti on the
streets and walls. '

' Less vandalism, especially on Donald Dewar.'

Eco-logic:

Many wishes pick up on Glasgow's heritage as a 'dear green place', and hope that people will take on the personal responsibility to make it a stronger reality by 2020. Fears of environmental doom are powerfully countered by a hope that Glasgow can innovate out of disaster.

' Everyone — today — to make changes in their lives to save our planet! Cars, litter, fumes, chemicals. 2020 to be clean.'

' My wish is that greater use is made of all the derelict and unused buildings within the city not just the '"centre".'

' Trees be planted down the middle of Victoria Road — Boulevard Victoria! It's a very wide road — loads of room… plant now for 2020!'

' I wish that all of Glasgow can develop the Clyde as a playground for the entire city with nature walks developed and playground areas for kids — a testament to the past and future of the city.'

' Every child should be able to see a duck on a sunny day. '

What is immediately striking about the seven clusters is the dominance of value-based issues — what could be called the social and emotional capital of cities.
The usual fare of local authority satisfaction surveys are there — crime, grime, health and education, but so also are other hopes, dreams and wishes that people spontaneously bring to the table in at least

equal numbers, and go well beyond the usual remit of consulting on what makes a place good or be better.

Confidence, niceness, openness, pride, freedom, happiness…these individual urban assets are identified in people's wishes, but often they are gathered together in a nuanced description of what the experience of living in Glasgow in 2020 should feel like. This could be seen as a little bit of a cheat — sneaking three wishes or more into one (a trick all genies are wise to) — but more importantly they give a captivating insight into what kinds of places people want to live in and share. With 2007 predicted to be the year when the birth of someone somewhere in the world tips the balance so that a majority of the world's population lives in urban areas, the need to find and share these hopes of how we want to live together becomes ever more important.

The question is, how well configured are Glasgow and other cities to meet these complex needs? The cross-government and local response to the liveability agenda in the late 1990s showed how our institutions can successfully respond and adjust to the emergence of a new set of issues. Michael Lyons' place-shaping agenda is also beginning to map out a different role for local councils and councillors. This could mean local authorities might be able to reach into some of the clusters of issues identified in Glasgow, which conventionally they have not felt legitimate or skilled to do. However, this is not just a challenge for government, but for business, the third sector and others. For example, one recurring theme, alongside people's impatience with government, was a frustration at the lack of responsibility shown by high-profile corporations in the city, who many felt played no real local civic role.

The messy cluster of hopes and wishes revealed by Glasgow 2020 do not sit easily or wholly with government or the private sector, and instead involve a significant level of individual responsibility and a broad concept of the public realm, blurring what is public and what is private.

TOP 10 WEBSITE WISHES

01. I wish that most of central Glasgow becomes car-free.
02. My wish is that Glasgow becomes a city of great artists with stunning architecture and a colourful street life with flower markets.
03. Everywhere I look I see beauty and not architectural rabbit hutches, gap sites, rubbish and cracked concrete pavements.
04. The Subway could be expanded to the South Side.
05. I wish that children of all ages will be safe to enjoy the city. It will be free of violence and litter.
06. One of my wishes for Glasgow's future is to see the Clyde's potential maximised. A tree-lined walkway from Braehead to Glasgow Green and back again on the other side. Boats and cruises to take you the length of the city, pubs and cafes on the river banks. Other cities the world over offer this — its time for Glasgow to do the same!
07. To walk into other areas without feeling threatened.
08. Less graffiti and litter — generally a more pleasant and tidy environment.
09. My wish is that Glasgow will be a city without fighting.
10. Glasgow recycles more waste and becomes more environmentally aware and responsible.

THE FUTURES
QUESTIONNAIRE.[109]   The new orthodoxy about how
we see ourselves and the
world around us asserts that we are a society of lucky
pessimists. This is a world view that can be summarised
as 'I'm doing alright and expect to do even better in
the future, but the rest of the world is going to hell in
a handcart '.

In one recent poll conducted by YouGov people
were asked whether they thought Great Britain today
was better than five years ago. Sixty-two per cent
thought it was worse, only 11 per cent thought it had got
better. Asked to look ahead and guess what Britain might
be like in five years' time, 53 per cent said it would be
worse and only 11 per cent thought it would be better.
However, when asked about their own lives in 2007 63
per cent described themselves as optimistic.[110]

This pessimism about our collective future is
equally evident in polling of people's perceptions about
the key institutions of the public realm such as health,
education and policing, where the pessimists outnumber
the optimists by roughly 2:1. For example, only 18 per
cent of people believe that the NHS is likely to improve
in the next few years, compared with 50 per cent of
people who think it will get worse.[111] This is despite
people having high levels of satisfaction with their
personal experience of sections of the NHS — one poll
found that over three-quarters of people are satisfied
with their GP.[112]

The danger here is that instead of seeing how
quality of life for individuals and families is integrally
related to the health of the 'commons', individual and

collective well-being have become disconnected. As Tom Bentley has written, there are a whole host of personal decisions where the wider consequences — social, cultural, environmental, economic — are treated as externalities and therefore not taken into consideration. For example in relation to the environment, through using plastic bags at supermarkets, taking cheap flights and driving children to school.[113]

These individualistic well-being strategies would be fine, but critically ignore their accumulative impact on the quality of the public realm — for example, if people disregard the cleanliness of a local park, its value to a community soon diminishes. Not only does this corrode the quality of the public realm, but it also undermines the quality of decisions and outcomes individuals can make and achieve.

For example, as more parents choose to drive their children to school they contribute to traffic congestion, which in turn makes the school run take longer and raises early-morning stress levels. At the same time they add to the pollution and traffic risk that made parents anxious about letting their children walk to school in the first place.

With the much-documented decline in trust and optimism towards so many of the institutions of the public realm, the challenge is to find new ways of decision-making and organising that can help reconnect individual and collective well-being by helping make choices visible, transparent and meaningful.[114]

An alternative to the lucky pessimist
In contrast to the dominant story of lucky pessimists, we found the beginning of a different pattern being

played out in Glasgow. In contrast to other collective institutions, people were largely optimistic about the future of their city. This potentially opens up a new more hopeful story about individual and collective well-being.

When asked whether they thought life would be worse or better in 2020 just under three-quarters of people said it would be better for them personally *and* Glasgow as a whole (table 1: respondents' views when asked whether life would be worse or better in 2020).

The future in 2020	Better	Worse	Net optimism
For individual	71.2	11	+ 60.2
For Glasgow	69	13.5	+ 55.5

The results for the city of Glasgow compares extremely well against people's perceptions of other collective institutions. Even education, generally the public service people tend to be most optimistic about, has scored at best a net optimism score of +10 in recent years.[115] The challenge for Glasgow is how to tap into this sense of optimism and activate the city as a meaningful and effective framework for collective action that links individual and collective well-being. The opportunity is there, but there are also warning signs that this will not be an easy or straightforward task.

Doubting neighbourhoods
An important bridging space between the city as a whole and individuals are Glasgow's neighbourhoods. While people do tend to be optimistic about the future of their neighbourhood, it is at a level significantly lower than their optimism about their own life or the future

as a whole (table 2: respondents' views when asked whether the neighbourhood would be worse or better in 2020).

The future in 2020	Better	Worse	Net optimism
For the neighbourhood	56.8	15.6	+41.2

In neighbourhoods people are likely to encounter other people on a level of intimacy not experienced as they move around the malls or the city centre. It is in neighbourhoods that people tend to feel most personally affected by litter, anti-social behaviour and a lack of trust in those they live near. It is here that people are more likely to feel the gap between the Glasgow branding slogan 'Scotland with Style' and their day-to-day lives.

It would be easy to slam the city's policy of the last 20 years, investing heavily in cultural regeneration of the city centre and in turn neglecting outlying neighbourhoods. However, as Garcia and Scullio found in their extensive research in the city,[116] there is widespread support for iconic cultural regeneration projects among Glasgow's working-class communities.

Nonetheless, our research found that people in disadvantaged neighbourhoods felt there was a sense of injustice — 'our neighbourhood isn't getting its fair share and is being left behind' — and a sense of frustration that people did not have any accessible ways to participate in Glasgow's good times. As such there is a struggle to find a shared story of optimism about the future that can connect the city, the neighbourhood and the individual. Cities — rather than nations or firms — have increasingly been recognised as the engines of economic growth and innovation. The tantalising question illuminated by the

Glasgow 2020 project is whether cities can also become recognised as engines of optimism and hope about our collective futures.

GROUP DISCUSSIONS
AND LOCAL FUTURES LITERACY. The questionnaires, stories and wishes showed that people in Glasgow are generally optimistic about the future of their city. But these came from individual perspectives. In discussion sessions different people came together to deliberate and draw up a variety of shared perspectives on the future.

The discussion revealed that across a range of issues there was a stark lack of a common vocabulary or language between different parts of the city. This was perhaps most pronounced between affluent, middle-class groups and less affluent, disadvantaged groups. The more middle-class groups tended to see the city as generally getting wealthier, and had a belief that this success percolated down to everyone. The more disadvantaged groups tended to see the whole city as being dominated by social housing and the acute social problems that they encountered daily.

The segregation of language and world views reflect the spatial segregation experienced by Glasgow and other cities in the UK; although relatively modest by international standards, this has accelerated over the last decade. As Dorling and Rees have shown, neighbourhoods are becoming more segregated on the basis of wealth, illness, premature mortality, educational opportunities and the availability of quality work.[117]

The discussion groups created matrixes to explore

possible changes, continuities, trends and events, and ranked them according to how likely and desirable people believed they were.

A number of patterns emerged from the matrixes themselves and the conversations they helped stimulate and structure.

Optimism [about the future]:

Confounding the common Scottish stereotype of the dour, fatalistic Scot, those who took part in the discussions exhibited distinctly optimistic tendencies. The most populated side of the matrix was consistently the 'desirable' right-hand side of the matrix, with the upper 'likely' quadrant also better filled than the bottom 'unlikely' quadrant. This perspective contrasted with 2020 sessions Demos ran with people in other cities. For example, in Helsinki change was seen as more unlikely to occur, with the status quo assumed to hold even if it was not seen to be desirable.

The way people talked about change and the future was heavily gendered, however. Generally, across most socio-economic backgrounds, women tended to speak of social change as being community-led, involving themselves and others, and bringing about tangible change. This helped to feed a view of the future that was broadly optimistic and more inclusive. Men, on the other hand, tended to think of social change as being about macro-politics and leaving decisions to politicians. This helped contribute to a more pessimistic view of the future among men in which they appeared to feel less powerful or able to shape their own destinies.

Uncertainty [about change]:
There was a widely felt recognition that the city had changed significantly in recent years and that this pace of change would continue. However, there was uncertainty about the impact of change, highlighting the need to separate out attitudes towards the future from attitudes to change. There was concern about inequality, and the extent to which disadvantaged or excluded communities would share in the positive changes. There was also a sense of disorientation engendered by the pace of change and a strong sense that progress had been far from linear or uniform:

' It's got better for gay people, but its got worse on race and religion.'

' It's a divided city that makes progress in one area, only for another division to assert itself elsewhere.'

' It's better for some, worse for others. Health is on the up, education is down.'

LIK

UNDESIRABLE

UNL

ELY

DESIRABLE

ELY

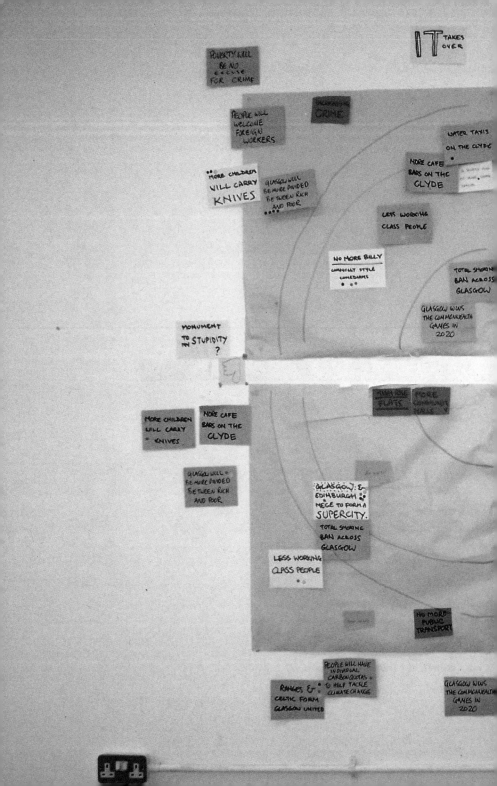

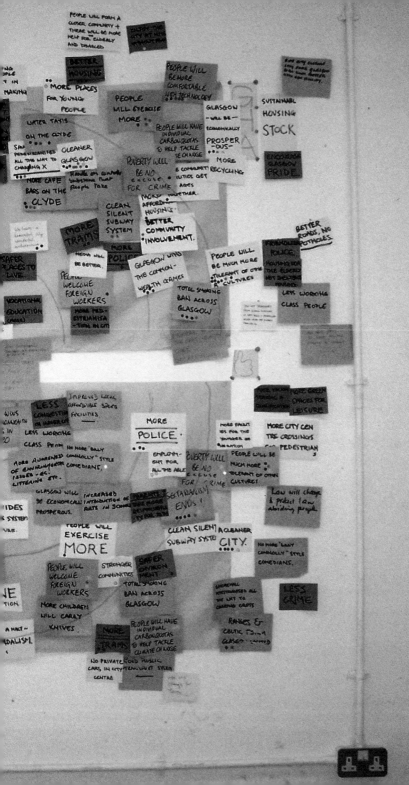

Confidence [in big projects]:

The cluster of elements that people tend to feel most confident about being likely to change relate to investments in infrastructure and big projects, for example, transport infrastructure, public buildings and housing improvements. However, there was some disquiet about whether this was sufficient to make a better Glasgow:

' You hope the people at the council have learnt that buildings don't change people.'

' The investment in all the physical stuff looks great, but it's not enough.'

' The city looks good but only in a marketing way.'

Frustration [with other people]:

Although the matrixes show the potential for a brighter future, it is a future hamstrung by other people. Group participants found it much harder to express confidence in positive transitions on aspects of the future that were more dependent on other people's behaviour. Reductions in violence, street crime, litter, vandalism, using cars less and exercising more, all tended to be consigned to the desirable but *unlikely* corner. In many of the conversations there was a sense that the city had lost patience with itself and was getting increasingly desperate:

' The city should contaminate the drug supply so when the junkies are jacking up they know there is a risk you might die. It might make some of them think again and get rid of a few of them.'

> ' Teenage single mothers should be sterilised to prevent them having children again.'

As reflected in these quotes, the response to the frustration with other people was often a resort to advocating tighter and tighter control by a strong-arm council. This was a theme picked up in other parts of the project. For example, many of the stories feature the council as an increasingly intrusive force in people's private lives, spying on them and penalising them for behaving in anti-social ways.

Recognition [of the need for new tools]:

Sectarian attitudes, the relentless carbon consumption of a city structured around shopping, bad parenting, alcohol abuse and the continual threat of violence often felt like intractable problems all caught up in other people's bad behaviour. For some people the only place they felt they could turn was the council and ever tougher crack-downs aimed at bringing other people into line. But just as many conversations about the future turned in a very different direction, towards an idea of self-help and self-organisation:

> ' The big chances for changes don't lie with the council —
> but with ourselves. We need to do stuff to live together
> better, and not just look to the political system to change us.'
> — Male Westender

> ' It's about a process for getting hope: we need to trust, to
> trust schools, children, ourselves. We need people in rooms
> talking. We need to understand ourselves. The community

needs to come together to change. We need people to take
control and volunteer themselves. We need hope but we
know it's hard.'
— Single mum, East End

' People start using their imagination and positive attitude to
change things for themselves. Teenagers stop complaining
they've got nothing to do and create things for themselves....
People start working on it and set example to others.'
— Male teenager, East End

' Through our attitude we make ourselves independent....
We need to define ourselves by being positive
about ourselves and break the cycle of the city's
inferiority complex.
— Female health worker

These reflections and hopes for the future point to
a radically different story of change. Rather than a
future hamstrung by other people's behaviour or being
dominated by all-powerful institutions, it has at its heart
a strong sense of individual responsibility and implies
new patterns of participation and of social cooperation.

PART
7

THE
OPEN
CITY

*' When the mood of the music changes,
the walls of the city shake.'*
— Late 1960s slogan, attributed to Plato [118]

The first step to a better future is imagining one.
Glasgow 2020 has been a practical experiment to
find an alternative to the closed city by opening up
Glasgow's future to the mass imagination of its citizens.
This chapter shares the storylines generated for the
future of Glasgow and explores what it and other cities
can learn from the process. It then asks how bottom-up
storylines can be turned into action and begins to map
out the core components of what it would mean for a
place to become a more *open city* in terms of everyday
governance, culture, design and planning. It concludes by
identifying a number of places of hope and imagination
in the city and sketches out the notion of 'assemblies of
hope' as one vessel to carry forth and nurture change.

POSSIBLE FUTURES.   The stories the people of
Glasgow created, the wishes cast
and the ideas exchanged did not create a single unifying
vision for the city. Instead a diverse set of storylines
emerged from which seven possible scenarios were
distilled to describe what Glasgow could be like in 2020.

The two-speed city:
By 2020 economic and social divisions are so entrenched
that Glasgow has become two cities living side by side
in blissful ignorance of one another. One half believes
that 'everyone is middle class now' while the other half
is bedded down in social housing estates, existing in

temporary jobs or on benefits. Both halves believe that they represent the majority experience of living in the city.

The two cities are self-replicating. With social mobility at an all-time low, people are born in the same side as they die. There are little to no movements between the two cities and the politics of Glasgow are entirely conducted around the values of the richer half. The excluded have by and large opted out of voting, politics and notions of citizenship.

The connected, cash-rich/time-poor part of the city is constantly in a rush. There are special toll roads, air-conditioned walkways and luxury water-taxis carrying people to and fro, cocooned from the rest of the city. The other half have to rely on crowded, dilapidated public transport. They have plenty of time but little to do, spending most of their time hidden away at home.

The soft city:

For years Glasgow's soft city — its sense of friendliness, nattering and blethering often led by women — had been constrained by the hard city of men. By 2018, the unchecked growth of drug addiction, violence and anti-social behaviour had reached crisis point. Glasgow looked to those excluded from the old-fashioned hard city of toxic masculinity: women campaigners and men prepared to align with them and change.

A city once renowned for masculine attitudes, behaviour and values, runs to a very different heartbeat. Women in Glasgow 2020 have formed the vanguard of a new cultural epoch, working in different, more co-operative ways. Many men enthusiastically sign up too, liberated from the pressures of machismo and competition.

Football is no longer so important — one sport among many. Glasgow has lost the chip on its shoulder, is making up with Edinburgh and reaching for peace with the wider world. It has even taken the step of apologising for its role in the British Empire, and brought a still lively Bill Clinton to the city to chair a Truth and Reconciliation Commission to mend sectarian disputes.

The dear green city:
What was once a gritty industrial place has now embraced the green life. As the price of energy spiralled out of control, Glasgow's fierce cultural independence and sense of itself has translated into a collective effort to go 'off-grid' and generate its own power.

Glasgow's green revolution sees exercise bikes hooked up to generators in schools, offices and homes, while windmills and solar panels top most buildings. 'Glasgondalas' now line up along the banks of the Clyde and special bikes have been developed to take the edge off riding up the hills.

The city leads the promotion of clean energy and sustainable living, exporting eco-friendly energy to the rest of Scotland and the world. With climate change causing a permanent drought down south, Glasgow is even managing to make a nice profit piping water to England.

The slow city:
By the early years of the twenty-first century, more Glasgow voices were starting to question the city's preoccupation with shopping, and its pride as the biggest retail centre outside of London. Glaswegians began to come down with consumption fatigue, and slowly turned

their back on the thrill of compulsive spending.

By 2020 many have abandoned preoccupations with wealth, conspicuous consumption and rewarding talent with money. Instead there is a widespread sense that there are more profound issues at stake: finding some deeper meaning to life, investing time and love in bringing up children, caring for neighbours, the vulnerable and the old.

It becomes a city that values slowness and deliberation over the fast. There is now a sense of pride in taking time doing things, doing jobs well, building products that last, and there is no longer a social stigma attached to therapists — you are weird if you *don't* have one. Yoga has replaced football as the city's exercise of choice, and the council sponsors offices to introduce siestas. Well slept, well exercised and well meaning; this is the new civic spirituality.

The lonely city:

The lonely city is an atomised, individualised, hi-tech future. People are free to create their own lives on their own terms. They work, play and socialise through their computers not needing to interact with anyone who isn't just like themselves. All communities are based around long-tail individual interests rather than shared geographical places.

Interactions with neighbours, people on the street and in shops have become an optional extra. Everything that Glaswegians used to rely on each other for (security, humour, ideas, companionship, even violence) can now be secured by relationships mediated through technology. The world is full of opportunities and possibilities, but for someone looking for a face-to-face friend, Glasgow feels like a lonely place.

This is a Glasgow where people seek meaning, satisfaction and freedom through technology and consumption, but where they do not make a connection between their lifestyle choices and the fragmented, empty nature of large parts of the city.

The hard city:

The city authorities ran out of patience with their people a long time ago. All efforts to support trust and community have failed. Government intervention extends into citizens' lives as never before, enforcing curfews on entire families, banning smoking in the home, and outlawing the use of petrol-driven cars. Children who break rules at schools are interned in youth detention centres outside the city known as Ned-Camps.

This is a city that is proud that it practises 'hard love', 'tough on failure and tough on the causes of failure'. Bigger and bigger sticks are needed to get people to respond and behave in the way government wants them to.

Teenagers are temporarily sterilised to prevent pregnancy and Asbo kids are named and shamed during prime-time TV ad-breaks. Neighbourhoods can take part in street-versus-street competitions text-voting out their favourite nuisance neighbour, who is then deprived of any rights to benefits or housing. As a consequence crime has dramatically reduced and the city is much neater, cleaner and quieter, apart from the constant growl from the police helicopters swirling overhead.

The kaleidoscope city:
Once so white with a predictable range of voices, accents, cultures and clothes, Glasgow has exploded into a kaleidoscope of diversity. The city is known for its open doors policy to newcomers and its tolerant cosmopolitan atmosphere. Waves of newcomers have arrived and been absorbed: the Poles, the Bulgarians, the Romanians, the Somalis, the Iraqis, the Lebanese...even the English are at home here now.

Immigrants have shaped the cuisine of and propelled Glasgow into the gastronomic premier league, while the pink pound has animated the city's nightlife. These changes have led to an unheralded degree of change, where the old divisions and identities are barely remembered by the younger generations and new Glaswegians. Partick Thistle has become the most successful football team in Glasgow, buoyed by the support of newcomers.

Learning from the possible futures:
What should Glasgow and other cities learn from these stories and Glasgow 2020? Part of the value of the mass imagination process proves to be less about setting out a neat sequence of events and predictions that lead inexorably and uniformly to a better, brighter, stronger future city, but rather how it prompts a re-interpretation of events in the present and helps reveal blind spots in current thinking and practice in cities. To quote Proust, 'The real voyage of discovery consists not in seeking new landscapes, but in having new eyes.' [119] Some of the main blindspots and rethinks the project revealed include:

- In the allocation and targeting of health resources our findings corroborate other research that advocates a shift away from just focusing on the material determinants of ill-health – such as unemployment and bad housing – and a shift towards addressing social and cultural determinants.[120]

- In how cities consult and engage with the public, there are again clear recommendations in terms of the need not just to open up areas of policy and decision-making to public participation, but also to involve the public in a dialogue about what questions get asked in the first place.

- There are also lessons about how a city develops its marketing strategy. Civic pride and a sense of authenticity and ownership among people already living in a city are just as important as chasing external media, businesses and tourists.

Underneath these specific insights is a broader lesson about the primacy of values — individual and collective — in the hope for better futures in cities. The goal of 'moving up the value chain' is central to the official future and tightly tied to creating an 'excellent economic environment'.[121] The strong emphasis given in the emergent futures to intangibles such as fairness, happiness, pace, confidence, pride and environmental justice point to a need to widen our understanding of how value chains work in cities.

Richard Layard's work has already prompted a rethink in policy and academic circles about the relationship between economic productivity and well-being by arguing that beyond a certain level of wealth, individuals are unable to translate increases in income to increases in levels of life satisfaction.[122] Offer's research points to the uncomfortable truth that affluence feeds impatience, and impatience creates unhappiness.[123] Elsewhere, Florida and Tinagli's research into the three Ts of talent, technology and tolerance suggests that we should flip the usual assumption of cause and effect: dynamic economies do not beget social cohesion; rather certain kinds of social cohesion and values can beget dynamic economies.[124]

The wishes collected revealed a clear conception of the personal attributes people thought they would need to thrive in the future, including confidence, openness and tolerance. Matching this, a number of the emergent futures set out visions of the 'good city' that reflect these individual values, including qualities such as openness, tolerance, ecological awareness and emotional intelligence. This suggests that people have a strong desire to get a better alignment between individual and collective values, and the emergent futures set out the kinds of contexts in which people feel they could thrive.

This symbiotic relationship between individuals and their environment is supported by self-determination theory, which asserts that three basic psychological needs (autonomy, competence and relatedness) are necessary for individual well-being. The assumption is that people have an innate tendency to grow these capacities but only within a supportive social context; individual knowledge and skills are not enough on their own.[125]

There are some clear implications for current policy in towns and cities where approaches to issues such as anti-social behaviour or encouraging green lifestyles tend to be couched in either a negative view of humans as inherently selfish and requiring the right sticks and carrots to behave 'correctly',[126] or that the problems facing people are not social, but the result of poor choices made by uni-formed or irresponsible individuals.[127] The experience in Glasgow suggests the beginning of a very different, values-led, basis for participation and engagement. As Ogilvy writes, 'human virtues are renewable resources', but they need to be created and sustained by practice and context.[128]

There is a further need for better upstream accounting and integration of the values that people hope our urban infrastructure can promote and their downstream impacts. Ravetz et al explored this idea in terms of 'total metabolism mapping' [129] and the stark disconnect it can reveal between the cities we want and the ones we get. For example, in transport, our upstream values are needs like access and opportunity. What we actually get are congestion and climate change, something that can be obscured by the tendency to focus on delivery and outputs such as more roads or increased public transport numbers.

In Glasgow this metabolism problem is evident in the provision of social housing. The upstream values people seek from homes are about security, comfort and retreat, but in the rush to deliver on these needs through repeated cycles of demolition and rebuild, often what people end up with is a sense of uncertainty, disempowerment and injustice.[130]

FROM STORYLINES
TO ACTION.
The question remains, how much can the closed city take on and use this kind of learning? There is a danger of little more than fine-tuning the closed city into a smarter, more sensitive, streetwise version of itself armed with a refreshed mental map to guide its official future, but essentially business as usual. Such an outcome would do little to broaden out what is in danger of being a cyclical revival of cities into a more sustainable and widely shared structural renewal.

The social geographer Susan Feinstein asked the critical question: 'Can we build the cities we want?' The emergent storylines generated through the process of mass imagination blend radical change and conservative nostalgia, a heady brew of hopes and fears for what the future might hold. Together they represent a significant opening up of the urban imagination about the kinds of lives — individual and collective — people hope are possible in our cities. At the same time, they expose a stark ingenuity gap between people's hoped for futures and the current set of tools and resources available to help get them there.

Progressing any of the emergent storylines — or averting any of them — requires more than just opening up space for non-institutional voices and storylines. It also requires finding new ways to mobilise communities of interest and action behind those storylines. It demands developing new patterns of participation and new patterns of producing collective goods. If the first step to better futures is imagining them, then the next steps are about developing the means of collaboration and innovation that help make those better futures possible. The experience of Glasgow provides some clues as to where and how these steps might be taken.

Urban gold mines

The 2020 project emerged in the gap between public institutions and people. This is a gap that is usually characterised by a lack of trust and connection, where fatalism and frustration pervade. But in this commonly negative space, people in Glasgow generated enthusiam and optimism, and brought into focus two potentially powerful resources for the future of cities.

The first resource is people — people as reciprocators who are disposed towards finding opportunities for social cooperation and self-improvement.[131] The second resource is the power of the city as a collective institution that people identify with and are optimistic about. This is a rare commodity compared with other public institutions from local authorities to the health service. Cities have become accepted as one of the primary units of economic growth and significant investment is now routed through them to promote economic productivity and innovation. Indeed part of the optimism that people feel is a result of the improving economic conditions of cities. But the city is far more than its economy, just as it is far more than city hall. People have an energy and passion for their city, they are proud of it and they care for it. At its best, the city is where people find recognition from others and where they feel that they matter. This pride and faith often comes in spite of how people feel about the council and whether or not they feel they are getting their fair share of the economic good times.

At the moment, the city as a shared idea and resource is called on only for marketing brochures and occasionally for mega events like the Olympics or Capital of Culture bids. The question is whether it can be mobilised in a more sustained way? And can a better connection be made between the city as a collective resource and the shift towards personal improvement? Significant investment has gone into stimulating and supporting economic innovation in cities. There is now a growing need to match this with equivalent investment in social and democratic innovation. Cities could be the ideal unit and site to focus this effort; small enough to be tangible yet large enough to affect change at a scale that matters.

The power of us — from mass imagination to mass collaboration

To help begin to close the gap between the cities people want and the cities people get requires looking beyond the structures and tools of the closed city. It is also perhaps not very helpful to look back to what many consider the last great age of cities in Britain, the Victorian period. Rather than industrial methods of organisation there is a need for responses that fit our post-industrial times and go further than either city boosterism or new localism.

One potential source of ideas for new ways of working is the emerging paradigm of user participation and production spurred by the Web 2.0 phase of development of the internet, which relies on the contributions and collaboration of many people to create content for others. As Benkler has described, while the industrial revolution centralised the means of production into large corporations and bureaucracies that had the capital and resources to achieve economies of scale, now a combination of cheap computers, new social software and distributed computing capacity, are starting to give production power back to people.[132]

According to Topscott, Williams and Sklar, these 'weapons of mass collaboration' are 'giving rise to powerful new models of production based on community, collaboration and self-organisation rather than on hierarchy and control'.[133] YouTube, Skype, Linux, flickr, Second Life, eBay and SETI@Home are all stars of this new era and have become household names.

WIKIPEDIA

The online encyclopaedia created and maintained almost entirely by amateurs now has over six millions' articles in 250 languages. It is guided by the philosophy that 'unmoderated collaboration among well-meaning, informed editors will gradually improve the encyclopaedia in its breadth, depth and accuracy'.[134] Maintenance tasks are performed by a group of volunteers; these include developers, who work on the software, and other trusted users with various permission levels including 'steward', 'bureaucrat' and 'administrator'.

THE SOUND OF MUSIC

In the last ten years the whole recording industry has been turned on its head by people who are able to make and exchange music on their own terms. The falling price of digital technology and recording software, combined with music blogging and the emergence of music-focused social networking sites like MySpace, have moved the distribution of music closer to people's hands. Whereas previously being 'signed' to a record label was a route to fame for musicians, now people are unlikely to be signed unless they have already attained a certain degree of fame among communities passing around and commenting on their music. In 2007 un-signed Enter Shikari's album reached number four in the UK charts, purely off the back of internet talk.

INNOCENTIVE NETWORK
Proving mass collaboration is not just something for left-field cyber warriors, US pharmaceutical giant Eli Lilly set up an online open R&D lab where 'seeker' companies and scientist problem-solvers interact in an eBay-like marketplace. A company posts a problem and a scientist offers a solution in return for a reward. Four years after it had set up over 90,000 scientists had signed up and over $1.5 million was paid out to bounty-hunter solvers. Bluechip firms like Dow Chemical, Dupont and Procter & Gamble have also signed up. The latter were prompted by a decision to outsource 50 per cent of new product and service R&D in order to help the company keep up with the pace of change in its sector. InnoCentive Chief Executive Darren J Carroll explains his motivation as 'trying for the democratisation of science'.[135]

FIGHTAIDS@HOME
Run on similar lines to SETI@home, which uses the downtime on personal computers to search for aliens, fightAIDS@home is the first biomedical distributed research computing project in the world. Run by the Olson Laboratory in California the project is powered by the World Community Grid which also powers other humanitarian projects. Free software downloaded by over thousands of people across the globe uses idle cycles of computers to help research the structural biology of Aids and develop new drugs.

As these developments show, individuals and groups of all shapes and sizes are beginning to take advantage of network communications, sharing effort and material resources in decentralised networks to solve problems — all without traditional managerialism of the state or large organisations.[136] Moreover, virtual collaboration is starting to leak into the physical world, with people pooling tangible resources such as cars through carpools, playing hybrid virtual-physical games such as *Cruel to be Kind*, *Assassin* and *Can You See Me Now*, and supporting change in the real world through sites such as PledgeBank with its strap line 'I'll change the world but only if you help me '.

So how might these self-organised patterns of collaboration and innovation begin to be applied to the organisation of cities? In some ways they are already embedded in their DNA. Warren Weaver's 1948 essay 'Science and complexity' [137] was probably the first sketching out of cities understood as complex systems, but it was Jane Jacobs who fully explored and popularised the idea. She described the 'street ballet' of the well-populated sidewalk, which provides a wide bandwidth for interactions and the flow of information between strangers. Together the self-organised collaboration of 'many eyes on the street' creates a public good — a sense of safety. As Jacobs wrote: 'Vital cities have a marvelous innate capability for understanding, communication, contriving and inventing what is required to combat their difficulties.' [138]

How many people does it take to change a city?
Understanding cities as complex systems means recognising a vital city is not in the gift of a planner or

top-down visionary at city hall, nor in the gift of a hero architect drafted in. Instead it depends on the thousands of everyday choices made by the people who decide to live, work, play, bring up a family or start a business there. In other words, the vibrancy and quality of any place depends on how successfully it mobilises the widespread participation of its people.

However, it is perhaps not that helpful to say that the renewal of cities will come from the participation of everyone who lives there. The gap between the lone hero architect or charismatic mayor and the mass participation and collaboration of everyone is large. We need some steps between the two if cities are to achieve more distributed patterns of participation and power.

Over 5000 people took part in Glasgow 2020, which amounts to around 1 per cent of the population of the city. Is 1 per cent enough to change a city? It sounds a low proportion but it could be an important beginning. It is worth remembering that out of Wikipedia's 4 million registered members it is the 47,000 active members among them who actually keep the encyclopaedia thriving with regular posts and edits — just over 1 per cent of its members. Those 5000 people in Glasgow — made up of teens, hairdressers, council officials, health professionals, artists, single parents, entrepreneurs, community activists and many more represent a new pattern of participation involving people outside, inside and between Glasgow's formal institutions of governance. The way in which these people are linked together, empowered and bridged with others could begin to build the stepping stones from mass imagination to mass collaboration, and with it a very different kind of city.[139]

BUILDING
THE OPEN CITY. Not all the workings of online mass
collaboration can be grafted onto
the planning, design and governance of cities. But two
aspects do hold particular potential to help structure a
more open city: peering and sharing.[140]

Peer-to-peer working offers an alternative to more
hierarchical approaches, including both what can seem
paternalistic public services and corporate command-
and-control. Peering tends to be a more egalitarian way
of collaborating, which can comfortably work with
participants who have a range of different motivations
(altruism, financial, learning). It also values and meshes
different skills, and supports the development of two-
way relationships between people. These are all valuable
commodities in cities wrestling with problems of low
voter turn out, isolation and segregation.

Online sharing of everything from intellectual
capital to spare processing capacity underlines the
fact that to facilitate collaboration there is a need for
shared resources. The vibrancy and dynamism of mass
collaboration to create entirely new kinds of shared
resources or commons makes a sharp contrast to the
story about the commons in cities, such as parks and
public services, which is often a story of scarcity,
pressure and loss.

Alongside the social value of sharing runs an
environmental imperative. Shared access to space, goods
and services rather than exclusive individual ownership
has the potential to be less resource intensive and to
deliver improvements to quality of life.[141] This is an issue
of growing importance as one of the main challenges

cities face is how to respond to climate change and the end of the age of cheap oil.

If we are serious about turning the kinds of storylines created by Glasgow through mass imagination into action there are then two critical dimensions of our cities which greater peering and sharing could help re-calibrated: space and power.

Space — from private to public

Social fragmentation, the decline in trust of other people, and the rise of private ownership and management is pulling space in our cities in two directions. At one end we find frictionless, neutral plazas, walkways and squares, which in trying to appeal to all, end up appealing to nobody. At the other end we find spaces built around niche consumer experiences that balkanise the public into different lifestyle, age, ethnic and spending power brackets.[142]

During the Glasgow 2020 project there was a strong sense that people wanted a different kind of space — an alternative to lowest-common denominator blandness on the one hand and extreme fragmentation on the other. For example, there was an almost palpable yearning for the reopening the Kelvingrove Art Gallery and Museum, which did reopen in August 2006 after being shut for extensive refurbishment. The Kelvingrove is a shared space, which is part of Glasgow's past and current day civic pride, where people feel they can go and meet and mingle with others without being defined just as a consumer.

If cities are to mobilize their citizens effectively, then more shared spaces like this are needed.

They form the basic building blocks for the city — places where people and groups can pool their resources and create new kinds of commons which meet their diverse needs and aspirations. If in a democracy dominated by representation the function of public space is to enable people to be seen, then in a democracy animated by collaboration the function of public space is that it should be used.

How these commons are nurtured cannot be left to either just the market or the state, but a more mixed economy combining some qualities of both and also emerging models such as social enterprise. For example, in Glasgow the council opted to establish its Culture and Leisure Department as an independent charitable trust. This was a bold step undertaken for largely financial reasons, but could yet yield innovative and more open ways to help develop the city's civic infrastructure.

Proposals for the open city — from private to public space:

Kulture Centres:
User-generated content has been at the heart of the internet's biggest success stories over the last couple of years — profiles on Facebook, tags logged on del. i.cious, videos uploaded on YouTube. The coming years will increasingly see the interaction with the virtual and physical world. Cities should be investing to make the most of this interaction by opening up access to the kinds of tools urbanites will need.

DIY Kulture Centres would be open houses of studios and workshops where people can turn their creative or civic ideas into reality. Staffed with experts to help and advise, people would be able to access all the cool tools they have ever wanted to and try out everything from woodwork, metal work and graphic design to photography and publishing. Aarhus in Denmark already has one — the Huset Kulturcenter is smart and chic and is a shared space and resource for everyone.[143] Meanwhile in California a number of public libraries have added saws, drills and screwdrivers to books and DVDs on the list of what they lend to people.[144]

Emphasising access over ownership in this way could be extended to other areas. Cities could encourage the spread of multi-service networks where communities share access to under-used workspaces, workshops and equipment. For example, a mobility network that includes car-sharing, buses on demand, lift-sharing and bikes.[145]

Raising the commons:
Over the past 20 years we have fallen in love with the blue space in our cities again. Instead of buildings designed to back away from stinking docks and murky canals, watersides have become the centrepiece in regeneration efforts. But just as our blue space was once neglected another commons currently lies wasted — our sky space. The Blue Nile song evocatively invited us to take 'A Walk across the Rooftops', conjuring up beautiful images of Glasgow, but the current reality is not so picturesque. Roofs are one of the great unused and uncared for land masses in cities, often just used for air conditioning plants and plumbing. Cities should reclaim them for shared public use with running tracks, green

roofs, solar energy, art installations and gardens.

The freedom of the city:

Places need to find ways to legitimately build a better sense of shared values between the city, neighbourhoods and individuals. While city marketers often talk about the brand values of a place (humorous, generous, outgoing are some of the values used to describe Glasgow) these rarely translate into anything practical or distinctive.

A democratically created Place Pact could be one way to set out the aspired values and the practical action they could mean at the level of the city as a whole, neighbourhoods and individuals. There is ground to build on here: Glasgow already has a system of Neighbourhood Charters which help local communities take action to clean up their neighbourhood and the 2006 local government white paper for England also mooted
the idea of local charters which may include things like setting priorities for service providers and community bodies.

A Place Pact would be broader and more organic — more in common with the Chartist's People's Charter and the Charter of the Forest than John Major's ill-fated Citizen's Charter. It could set out the common values of the city and suggest what they mean in terms of voluntary action by people, neighbourhoods and businesses and public institutions. For example: in Glasgow one of the strong themes was a desire for the city to live up to its name as a *Dear Green Place*. Banning plastic bags, getting a green energy supplier, sourcing local food, walking more are all actions that a quango, a business, a household, or an individual can commit to doing.

Place Pacts will not work or be legitimate if they are issued by city hall. They would need to emerge from the type of deliberative, distributed and creative discussions used during Glasgow 2020. The values and practical ideas could be written by individuals or groups and then 'signed up to' by other people, providing a space for learning and collective efficacy, helping build solidarity around shared values rather than performance targets. They could draw on advances made by pledgebank.com, the Global Ideas Bank and the wishes rating system on the Glasgow 2020.

Public city:
Cities could have a public holiday for citizens taking the form of two days annually set aside for a city's residents to enjoy and celebrate everything they love about their city and/or volunteer for civic activities. Everything would be free with open access for residents — transport, exhibitions, private members' clubs and gyms.
Two days are necessary so workers in the service and leisure sectors get at least one day off. The Public City days expand on the successful 'Open Doors' programme,[146] where once a year public and private buildings — from synagogues to factories — throw open their doors to the public.

Power — from institutional to personal power
Shifting the balance from institutional to personal power in cities is less about what central government or city hall chooses to devolve to neighbourhoods and communities

but more about what people can grow and create for themselves and what resources they need to do it.

When people think about the future of their city they do not just hope for a better physical environment, they also hope for better humans. Glasgow 2020 found a clear set of mental aptitudes and skills that people think they will need in order to thrive in the future city. Investing in personal capabilities is an area of growing interest. The UK government's 2005 Equalities Review outlined a set of capabilities individuals should have, which included the capability to engage in productive and valued activities and the capability of being and expressing yourself, and having self-respect.[147]

Elsewhere, Gardner has recently written about the essential 'Five Minds for the Future' that people need to have 'both so we can survive as a species and so we can have a world that we'd want to live in'.[148] The five minds he advocates nurturing are:

- the disciplined mind, which is schooled in basic subjects but also a master of a profession, vocation or craft
- the synthesising mind, which makes sense of disparate and complex information
- the creating mind, which asks new questions and finds imaginative answers
- the respectful mind, which appreciates and engages with different cultures
- the ethical mind, which enables responsible behaviour as a citizen.

Can more open cities provide the context and means

by which investing in better human performance also improves collective well-being? The critical issue here is how improvements in individual capabilities — or power — aggregate to serve collective ends. At the moment a perverse opposite is occurring where our urban environments are in some important ways actually disempowering individuals. For example, a recent study of 4.4 million adults in Sweden found that the incidence rates of psychosis and depression rose in proportion with increasing levels of urbanisation.[149]

The following proposals all aim to increase the producer power of individuals by investing in the capacity and resources for social cooperation and collaboration. They bring together individual values and capabilities, and create a sense of shared context to realise and actualise them.

Proposals for the open city —
from institutional to personal power:

City bonds:
While still popular in other countries, particularly cities in the US; to help raise funds for infrastructure projects, bonds have fallen out of favour in the UK since their Victorian heyday. However, with some remodelling they could become an innovative form of participative civic pride.

Cities could have an open slate of civic projects that are identified by public nominations and online voting. These could be as small as supporting a community allotment or city festival, or as big as building a new concert hall. Once projects have crossed the threshold of a specified number of votes and have been vetted by a peer panel, they go on the official list and qualify for city bond support. Individuals, community groups, companies and public sector organisations would be able to support a favourite project through buying financial bonds or contributing their time and skills with time-bank bonds.

Cities could agree to distribute a percentage of Section 106 monies as city bonds, helping to open up and democratise this contested and opaque development tool. To help incentivise the system people could opt for a percentage of their council tax bills to be set aside for city bond projects. Time-bank bonds could also earn people money off their council tax bills.

The benefit of the city bond is that it allows people to participate in shaping a city's development priorities in a less blunt and more tangible and sustained way than just voting. It also gives public, private, civic organisations and individuals a transparent and more egalitarian way of contributing to collective projects.

Self-build neighbourhoods:

We continue to fail to get the housing we deserve — just 6 per cent of new build was rated as good or very good by one recent survey in one part of the UK.[150] An alternative is a greater role for self-build. Experience elsewhere in Europe shows self-build encourages quality and social interaction. Self-builders tend to invest the 'profit' from lower production costs (compared to off-the-shelf products built by volume house builders) in environmental innovation and better design.[151] Self-builders currently represent 13 per cent of new housing supply, which means it is already larger than the output of the largest volume house builder in the UK. But perhaps even more significantly is the evidence that up to 70 per cent of house buyers would consider self-build if they could.

Within Glasgow, there is already some evidence of people beginning to see this as a viable way forward. A group of ten families in Easterhouse (the Collree Self Build Housing Association)[152] have nearly completed the design and build of their own homes with the support of the local housing association and a firm of architects. However, at the moment most self-build is limited to single plots because of a lack of supply of land and the domination of volume house builders.

Cities could commit to making a percentage of new build in their boundaries self-build. This could be set at a minimum of 10 per cent, a figure viewed by a Joseph Rowntree report on self-build as achievable, and could then grow further with demand.[153] Such a move would need to be supported by changes to land provision, planning policy and practice, the adoption of new technologies and a modernisation of the self-build industry.[154]

Producer aid:
A good idea and people's enthusiasm can quickly get squashed once they run up against paperwork and regulation. For example, if a group of neighbours wants to run a community festival they suddenly find waste management plans, risk assessments, licence applications, and even flood-risk assessments need to be filled out.

Producer aid would provide a bank of skills and time from which individuals and groups can apply for the professional help they need to make an idea real. It would work in a similar way to legal aid, which provides services to people without the resources to pay for their own legal representation. Professional aid would be given to support people through insurance, licensing and health and safety processes, and build people's skills in the process.

PLACES OF HOPE

In Glasgow we found a clutch of spaces that worked as productive commons – shared spaces that brought people together and fostered collaboration. The Places of Hope represent a mixture of institutions, networks and activities beyond the mainstream: imaginative public organisations and spaces, and creative companies. They cover a range and scale of projects, organisations and networks, but some common themes run through many of them. One of them is a sense of openness and new or once marginalised communities (Glasgow Mela, Glasgow Women's Library); another is the importance of supporting children and parents (Jeely Piece Club); another is the belief in the efficacy of networks to facilitate activism (Glasgow User Manual, Critical Mass); the personalised use of public space (Sandyford, Saltire Centre); the power and publicness of art (Castlemilk Environment Trust, Studio Warehouse); and the importance of a design aesthetic and style (Matthew Algie, Linn). Some of these places and spaces have a sense of 'fuzzy' power, some are deeply collaborative, others enterprising. None of them sits in the conventional mainstream, or has anything other than character and uniqueness.

1. KELVINGROVE ART GALLERY AND MUSEUM

One of Glasgow's most prominent and loved institutions, Kelvingrove opened in 1901 as part of Glasgow International Exhibition. It is a favourite of local people and a popular tourist attraction providing a connection between the city's civic traditions and pride and how people see the city today. It was recently reopened after a multimillion pound refurbishment. www.glasgowmuseums.com/venue/index.cfm?venueid=4

2. GLASGOW WOMEN'S LIBRARY

Growing out of an arts project, Women in Profile, Glasgow Women's Library was set up in 1991. It is a unique resource in Scotland and the UK providing an archive and information, and undertaking research and events on women's experiences, culture and histories. www.womenslibrary.org.uk

3. STUDIO WAREHOUSE GLASGOW

This maze of independent studios and galleries in what was previously a warehouse and industrial space used the publicity and status of attracting the Paris-based Comme des Garcons 'guerilla store' in 2006 to establish and expand its site. www.swg3.tv

4. MONO AND MONORAIL

A bar and vegetarian food shop sit beside a live venue for bands (Mono) and independent record store (Monorail), in the east end of the city centre. There is something collaborative, warm and welcoming about this space with a cool, laid-back attitude and free wi-fi (as distinct from most commercial places in the city). www.rampantscotland.com/besteating/best_eating_dev_mono.htm

5. HIDDEN GLASGOW

This small group of dedicated amateur historians make it their mission to catalogue some of the less well-known aspects of Glasgow's industrial past, photographing and saving for posterity images of some of its forgotten buildings and institutions, and organising walks and talks about the city, past, present and future. www.hiddenglasgow.com

6. GALGAEL TRUST

Galgael Trust is known as Galgael or Gal-Gaidheil and based in Govan, from where they build wooden boats in celebration of the Clyde's heritage. 'The Gift of the Gael' was their first full-size boat, launched on New Year's Day 2000. They have built many smaller pieces — rowboats, carvings, furniture — and all their ventures aim to have a focal point for the community, involve learning and enriching people's lives and give the river back to the people. www.galgael.org

7. THE JEELY PIECE CLUB

The club has been active in Castlemilk since 1975 to improve the lives of children and parents. Now based in new premises it provides support for pre-fives in The Jeely Nursery and for 5–12-year-olds in The Jeely Playzone. It encourages parents to assist staff in the club's activities, aims to identify different ways to help parents be parents, and has a well-respected outreach programme in the area. www.glasgow.gov.uk/en/YoungGlasgow/ Under12/Activities/PlayCentres/Jeely+Piece.htm

8. GLASGOW CALEDONIAN UNIVERSITY SALTIRE CENTRE

Situated in Glasgow Caledonian's city centre campus, the Saltire Centre opened in 2005 and provides a learning environment with different spaces to meet different needs — from social interaction to group work and places for silent study. Within a stunning architectural and design setting, there is a one-stop advice shop, connectivity for students and members of the public, and commissioned public works of art by Toby Paterson and Gary Breeze. www.gcal.ac.uk/thesaltirecentre

9. CRITICAL MASS

A green campaigning and cycling group whose members cycle through Glasgow city centre once a month at a slow, steady speed to change the traffic pace with a loud beatbox announcing their presence. www.citystrolls.com

10. SANDYFORD INITIATIVE

A sexual health service with a difference. Sandyford provides a welcoming, personalised space and a model of public health which addresses sexual health in a holistic and non-stigmatising way. For an area that has long proven controversial in the west of Scotland Sandyford has won international attention and plaudits. www.sandyford.org

11. GLASGOW MELA
The largest multi-cultural festival in Scotland celebrating the music and dance of the South Asian sub-continent. Established in 2001, 'mela' means 'gathering' in Sanskrit. It offers an inspiring day of fun and festivities ranging from Bhangra to Russian folk and reggae, henna painting, curry and kulfi. www.glasgowmela.org.uk

12. LINN PRODUCTS AND RECORDS
Linn Products is an independent engineering company specialising in producing some of the best hi-fi in the world. Based in a Richard Rogers designed headquarters in Waterfoot, outside the city, its training office as well as Linn Records is in Castlemilk. The label has a track record of nurturing talent in classical and jazz music — and gave the Glasgow band The Blue Nile their breakthrough. www.linn.co.uk

13. CASTLEMILK ENVIRONMENT TRUST
A local charity that aims to improve the environment for its inhabitants. This is linked to the large open space network of Castlemilk. The Trust looks at issues of access, health, biodiversity, public art, conservation, landscape sustainability, maintenance and management, with the goal of aiding regeneration, and has even brought Yoko Ono's art to Castlemilk! www.castlemilkenvironmenttrust.org.uk

14. GLASGOW USER MANUAL
This is a community activist network for sharing resources and initiating campaigns to, in its words, 'halt the erosion of our communities' and prevent the city's 'neighbourhoods becoming 'catchments for the benefits of the mortgage broker '. www.glasgowusermanual.com

15. MATTHEW ALGIE
The UK's leading independent coffee roaster founded by Matthew Algie in 1864, which to this day remains a family-run business

located on the city's southside. Promoting great coffee (and tea) they support fair trade and have entered into partnership with Oxfam to open a new chain of coffee bars serving the best coffee called 'Progreso'. www.matthewalgie.com

16. HAMPDEN PARK
This is one of the most loved and revered places in Glasgow and Scotland. The national football stadium and home of Queens Park FC and a place where Glasgow transcends the football divide (except when the Old Firm are playing each other on cup days). Scene of the most enthralling European Cup Final of all time when Real Madrid beat Eintracht Frankfurt 7:3 in 1960, as well as the 1976 and 2002 finals. www.hampdenpark.co.uk

Assemblies of Hope:
Findings ways to nurture creative projects is crucial to aiding the birth of the open city.

If cities are to develop more shared stories about their future then they will need to invest in spaces, forums, contexts and experiences where people can go to beyond their usual circle of family, friends, neighbours and work colleagues. Cities need places where people can develop and swap ideas and stories about the future, as well as develop the skills and relationships needed to progress them. 'Assemblies of hope' could provide one way for people to develop shared goals and dreams and provide the conditions for the creative responses that could make them real.

In a recent paper addressing arts and cultural leadership, Graham Leicester came up with the idea of 'academies of hope'.[155] Two years ago Scotland 2020 also identified how hope is generated through storytelling, aiding people's capacity to believe they can bring about change. In Scotland, the notion of 'assemblies' carries with it the power of Robert Crawford's poem, 'A Scottish Assembly' and so grounds it in contemporary cultural identities.

'Assemblies of hope' would be spaces where artists, activists, entrepreneurs, people with environmental concerns, business people, public officials and people from no sector could find peer support, encouragement and hope.[156] They would aspire to open up a space for imagination and non-institutional thinking, and provide activities such as mentoring, discussions, shadowing, developing ideas and fostering collaboration in practical projects. They would create ideas, and search for ways to make them happen.

A mix of resources would be needed, from public and private sector agencies committed to supporting a reflective, independent space within the city, and augmented by new funding models such as social enterprise — an assembly of hope could not be owned by a single institution or party. In most cities there are collections of people and activities that offer some of the functions described above; the task for new 'assemblies of hope' would be to draw this energy together, and ensure that it is more than the sum of its individual parts.

NOT THE END. Glasgow 2020 was a bold and imaginative experiment, using public space and public conversation to explore mass imagination and the idea of hope in the context of the city. The city and futures that surfaced point in a very different direction from much urban policy with its emphasis on competition, big developments and the language of economic step-change and transformation.

The historian Lewis Mumford wrote in his celebrated *The City in History* of the city not just as a place of economic calculus and exchange, but as a place of love and empathy:

> ' For the city should be an organ of love; and
> the best economy of cities is the care and culture
> of men.' [157]

We have tried to set out the beginning of a manifesto for the open city, a city that takes on something of Mumford's proposition. Glasgow 2020 has shown that people have the imagination to create their own stories, filled with hope of future worlds and possibilities. The challenge continues to give voice and life to such dreams.

1 G Hassan, E Gibb and L Howland (eds), *Scotland 2020: Hopeful stories for a northern nation* (London: Demos 2005).

2 Quoted in P Hall, *Cities in Civilization* (London: Weidenfeld and Nicholson, 1998).

3 Rampant Scotland, 'Scottish place names around the world', see www.rampantscotland.com/placenames (accessed 27 Apr 2007).

4 P Hanlon, D Walsh and B Whyte, *Let Glasgow Flourish* (Glasgow: Glasgow Centre for Population Health, 2006).

5 Ibid.

6 W McIlvanney, 'Where Greta Garbo wouldn't have been alone', reprinted in W McIlvanney, *Surviving the Shipwreck* (Edinburgh: Mainstream, 1991).

7 SG Checkland, *The Upas Tree: Glasgow 1875–1975* (Glasgow: Glasgow University Press, 1976).

8 *1951 Census of Scotland*, General volume: Population, Age, Sex and Conjugal Condition, Birthplace and Nationality, Gaelic-Speaking Population and Housing (etc) (Edinburgh: HMSO, 1951).

9 Glasgow is the largest city in Scotland with an official population of 578,790 within its boundaries. There are several Glasgows, however — and the greater Glasgow conurbation is one of the biggest in the UK – with more than 1.1 million people. The Glasgow travel to work region contains 1.6 million people – nearly one-third of Scotland's population.

10 M Keating, *The City That Refused To Die: Glasgow: The politics of urban regeneration* (Aberdeen: Aberdeen University Press, 1991).

11 G Kerevan, 'It's surprising what you can buy from an ice-cream van in Scotland's Manhattan', *Spectator*, 17 Nov 2006.

12 Organisation for Economic Co-operation and Development, Urban renaissance: Glasgow: lessons for innovation and implementation, 2002, see www.oecd.org/LongAbstract/0,2546,en_33873108_33873870_2489481_1_1_1_1,00.html (accessed 27 Apr 2007).

13 *Foder's Scotland*, 20th edn, quoted in Glasgow City Marketing Bureau, *Scotland with Style* (Glasgow: Glasgow City Marketing Bureau, 2006).

14 I Turok and N Bailey, 'Glasgow's recent trajectory: partial recovery and its consequences' in D Newlands, M Danson and J McCarthy (eds), *Divided Scotland?: The nature, causes and consequences of economic disparities within Scotland* (London: Ashgate, 2004).

15 'Scottish retailing rivals', *The Economist*, 11 Mar 2004.

16 Glasgow City Marketing Bureau, 'Glasgow's tourism strategy 2006 public consultation document', see www.scotexchange.net/print/glasgow_s_tourism_strategy_public_consultation_jan_2007.pdf (accessed 27 Apr 2007).

17 Ibid.

18 Authors' interview with Michael Kelly, March 2006.

19 Glasgow City Marketing Bureau, 'Frommer's names Glasgow as one of its top ten must-see destinations for 2006', 11 Jan 2006, see www.seeglasgow.com/media-office/news-archive/january-june2006/frommers-names-glasgow-must-see-destination (accessed 27 Apr 2007).

20 Glasgow City Marketing Bureau, 'Glasgow voted UK's favorite city by readers of Conde Nast Traveller', press release, 4 Sep 2006, see www.seeglasgow.com/media-office/news-archive/july-december2006/glasgow-voted-uks-favourite-city (accessed 27 Apr 2007).

21 For full information, see www.glasgow2014.com (accessed 27 Apr 2007).

22 F McLay (ed) *Workers City: The real Glasgow stands up* (Glasgow: Clydeside Press, 1988); F McLay (ed) *The Reckoning: Public loss private gain* (Glasgow: Clydeside Press, 1990).

23 I Spring, *Phantom Village: The myth of the new Glasgow* (Edinburgh: Polygon, 1990).

24 Joan Anton of Fundacio RTF, speaking at BCN-LDN 2020, June 2006.

25 Rate of Population Change Dundee (% over previous 10 years – 1980–2001), Great Britain Historical GIS Project, see www.visionofbritain.org.uk/data_rate_page.jsp?u_id=10150553&c_id=10090283&data_theme=T_POP&id=1 (accessed 22 April 2007). Rate of Population Change Manchester (% over previous 10 years – 1980–2001), Great Britain Historical GIS Project, see www.visionofbritain.org.uk/data_rate_page.jsp?u_id=10033007&c_id=10001043&data_

theme=T_POP&id=1 (accessed 22 Apr 2007).

26 S Jenkins, *Thatcher and Sons: A revolution in three acts* (London: Allen Lane, 2006).

27 G Hassan, 'Labour, concepts of Britishness, "nation" and "state"' in G Hassan (ed), *After Blair: Politics after the New Labour decade* (London: Lawrence and Wishart, 2007).

28 For more information on the Birmingham Community Empowerment Network see www.bcen.net/ (accessed 27 Apr 2007).

29 G MacLeod, *From Urban Entreprenurialism to the Revanchavist City? On spatial injustice in Glasgow's renaissance* (Oxford: Blackwells, 2002).

30 Eurodirect, 'Who wants to marry a millionaire?' 3 July 2006, see www.eurodirect.co.uk/Pages/PR_Baby%20Millionaires.html (accessed 27 Apr 2007).

31 J Watson, 'Nation's top street suits golfers to a tee', *Scotland on Sunday*, 18 Mar 2007, see http://scotlandonsunday.scotsman.com/index.cfm?id=421372007 (accessed 27 Apr 2007).

32 Hanlon et al, *Let Glasgow Flourish*.

33 Ibid.

34 SLIMS Labour Market Intelligence Services, Glasgow 2006 Labour Market Statement, see www.researchonline.org.uk/fskills/doc/B2161.pdf?id=3394711&location=VOLUME3&extension=.pdf&pageCount=1&contentType=application/pdf (accessed 22 Apr 2007).

35 Ibid.

36 M Thompson-Fawcett, 'Reinventing the tenement: transformation of Crown Street in the Gorbals, Glasgow', *Journal of Urban Design* 9, no 2, Jun 2004.

37 'Friend of Zanetti', 'Contructing neoliberal Glasgow: the privatisation of public space', *Variant* 25, Spring 2006, see www.variant.randomstate.org/issue25.html (accessed 27 Apr 2007).

38 Ibid.

39 Ibid.

40 J Harkin and P Skidmore, *Grown Up Trust* (London: Demos, 2005).

41 D Leask, 'The high price of Scotland's drink and blade culture', *Herald*, 1 Apr 2007, see http://election.theherald.co.uk/homepage/electionfocus/display.var.1300768.0.0.php (accessed 27 Apr 2007).

42 J Maxmin and S Zuboff, *The Support Economy: Why corporations are failing individuals and the next episode of capitalism* (London: Allen Lane, 2002).

43 D Kavanagh and D Butler, *The British General Election of 2005* (Basingstoke: Macmillan Palgave, 2005).

44 B Rodgers, 'Turnout is really about class', *Guardian*, 14 May 2005, see www.ippr.org.uk/articles/index.asp?id=1486(accessed 22 Apr 2007).

45 Hanlon et al, *Let Glasgow Flourish*.

46 G Hassan and D Fraser, *The Political Guide to Modern Scotland: People, places and power* (London: Politco's Publishing, 2004).

47 R Sennett, 'The open city', Urban Age, see www.urban-age.net/0_downloads/Berlin_Richard_Sennett_2006-The_Open_City.pdf (accessed 27 Apr 2007).

48 Ibid.

49 Ibid.

50 C Musson, 'Why we never stood a chance', *Evening Times*, 30 Jan 2007.

51 I Calvino, *Invisible Cities* (London: Vintage Books 1997).

52 J Ogilvy, *Creating Better Futures: Scenario planning as a tool for a better tomorrow* (Oxford: Oxford University Press, 2002).

53 See earlier reference to 2014 Commonwealth Games bid.

54 WG Beaton, *Glasgow: Our City: Yesterday, today and tomorrow* (Glasgow: Corporation of Glasgow Education Department, 1957).

55 Glasgow Economic Forum, *A Step Change for Glasgow: Glasgow's ten year economic development strategy* (Glasgow: Glasgow Economic Forum, 2006).

56 Glasgow Community Planning Partnership, *Our Vision 2005–2010* (Glasgow: Glasgow Community Planning Partnership, 2005), see www.glasgowcommunityplanningpartnership.org.uk/FileAccess.aspx?id=19 (accessed 22 Apr 2007).

57 Ibid.

58 Glasgow Economic Forum, *Step Change for Glasgow*.

59 Ibid.

60 C Roxburgh, 'Hidden flaws in strategy', *McKinsey Quarterly* 2, 2003.

61 D Aaronson (ed) *Worldchanging: A user's guide to the 21st century* (New York: Abrams, 2006).

62 Glasgow Economic Forum, *Step Change for Glasgow.*

63 SLIMS Labour Market Intelligence Services, Glasgow 2006 Labour Market Statement.

64 N Guy, 'Looking ahead' in Glasgow City Council, Scottish Enterprise Glasgow and Glasgow Economic Forum, *Glasgow Economic Review: State of the city economy* conference (2006).

65 G Clark, 'Facing the city' in Glasgow City Council et al, *Glasgow Economic Review.*

66 Glasgow City Marketing Bureau 2006, *Image and Brand*, see www.seeglasgow.com/glasgow-the-brand/tourismstrategy/image-and-brand (accessed 27 Apr 2007).

67 Glasgow Economic Forum, *Step Change for Glasgow.*

68 Glasgow City Marketing Bureau, *New Advertising Creative Lauched [sic] for Glasgow: Scotland with style branding campaign*, 10 Apr 2006, see www.seeglasgow.com/media-office/news-archive/january-june2006/new-advertising-creative-lauched-for-glasgow (accessed 27 Apr 2007).

69 M Shaw et al, *The Widening Gap: Health inequalities in Britain* (London: Policy Press, 1999).

70 Hassan and Fraser, *Political Guide to Modern Scotland*; Shettleston disappeared as a result of boundary changes in the 2005 UK general election and its successor seat Glasgow Central had a turnout of 43.9%, the fifth lowest in the UK – Kavanagh and Butler, *British General Election of 2005.*

71 Glasgow Panel Survey 6, Ipsos MORI, March–April 2006.

72 WR Fisher, 'The narrative paradigm: in the beginning', *Journal of Communication* 35, no 4, fall 1985.

73 E Morgan, 'A city' in H Whyte (ed), *Mungo's Tongues: Glasgow Poems 1630–1990* (Edinburgh: Mainstream, 1993).

74 H Porter Abott, *The Cambridge Introduction to Narrative* (Cambridge: Cambridge University Press, 2002).

75 R McKee, *Story: Substance, structure, style and the principles of screenwriting* (London: Harper Collins, 1997).

76 C Booker, *The Seven Basic Plots: Why stories matter* (London: Continuum, 2004),

Part 1, passim.

77 Ibid.

78 S Denning, *The Leader's Guide to Storytelling: Mastering the art and discipline of business narrative* (New Jersey: Jossey-Bass, 2002).

79 D Pink, *A Whole New Mind: How to thrive in the new conceptual age* (London: Cyan Books, 2006).

80 A Simmons, *The Story Factor: Inspiration, influence and persuasion through the art of storytelling* (New York: Basic Books, 2006).

81 Fisher, 'Narrative paradigm'; also W Fisher, *Human Communication as Narration: Toward a philosophy of reason, value and action* (Carolina: University of South Carolina Press, 1987).

82 JS Seely Brown, S Denning, K Groh and L Prusak, *Storytelling in Organizations: Why storytelling is transforming 21st century organizations and management* (Butterworth Heinemann, 2004).

83 Ibid.

84 T Greenhalgh and A Collard; *Narrative Based Health Care: Sharing stories, a multiprofessional workbook* (London: BMJ Books, 2003).

85 Ibid.

86 NHS Greater Glasgow and Clyde, 'Launch of Scotland's first book prescription scheme', see www.nhsgg.org.uk/content/default.asp?page=s765_3&newsid=2251&back=s8_1 (accessed 27 Apr 2007).

87 L Mumford, *The City in History: Its origins, its transformation and its prospects* (London: Harcourt, 1961).

88 Booker, *Seven Basic Plots.*

89 Quoted in P Hubbard, *The City* (London: Routledge, 2006).

90 Ibid.

91 Glasgow City Council, 'The friendly city', see www.glasgow.gov.uk/en/AboutGlasgow/Touristattractions/thefriendlycity.htm (accessed 22 Apr 2007).

92 S Baxter, *The Omnibus Parliamo Glasgow* (Edinburgh: Birlinn, 1992).

93 M Munro, *The Patter* (Glasgow: Glasgow District Libraries, 1985).

94 Deacon Blue, *Raintown* (London: Columbia Records, 1987).

95 The Blue Nile, *A Walk Across the Rooftops*

(Glasgow: Linn Records 1984).

96 M Bell, No Mean City, see www.taggart-fanclub.co.uk/nomean.htm (accessed 22 Apr 2007).

97 M Burgess, Imagine a City: Glasgow in fiction (Glendaruel: Argyll, 1998).

98 BBC, 'London freesheet battle commences', 30 Aug 2006, http://news.bbc.co.uk/1/hi/business/5297416.stm (accessed 27 Apr 2007).

99 Scottish Blogs; Glasgow blogs, see www.scottishblogs.co.uk/glasgow.php (accessed 22 Apr 2007).

100 Gadget Vicar, see www.gadgetvicar.typepad.com/ (accessed 22 Apr 2007).

101 I Dream of Haggis, see http://idreamofhaggis.blogspot.com/ (accessed 22 Apr 2007).

102 Tartan Hero, see www.tartanhero.blogspot.com (accessed 22 Apr 2007).

103 H Kahn and AJ Wiener, The Year 2000: A framework for speculation on the next thirty three years (New York: Hudson Institute/Macmillan, 1967).

104 MA Hajer and A Reijndorp, In Search of the New Public Domain (Rotterdam: NAI, 2002).

105 P Galison, Image and Logic: A material culture of microphysics (Chicago: Chicago University Press, 1997).

106 See www.glasgow2020.co.uk (accessed 22 Apr 2007).

107 See BG Glaser and AL Strauss, The Discovery of Grounded Theory: Strategies for qualitative research (Chicago: Aldine Publishing Company, 1967).

108 Croft No 5. Talk of the Future, Album Sleeve Notes (Planet Five Records, 2004).

109 Question sample of 270 adults and young people.

110 YouGov/Sunday Times Survey Results, Dec 2006, see www.yougov.com/archives/pdf/STI060101007_1.pdf (accessed 27 Apr 2007).

111 See www.ipsos-mori.com/polls/2006/mdi060910.shtml (accessed 27 Apr 2007).

112 See www.yougov.com/archives/pdf/OMI050101083_1.pdf (accessed 27 Apr 2007).

113 T Bentley, Building Everyday Democracy (London: Demos, 2005).

114 Ibid.

115 Government Delivery Index, IPSOS MORI, Sep 2006, see www.ipsos-mori.com/polls/2006/mdi060910.shtml (accessed 27 Apr 2007).

116 B Garcia and A Scullion, Glasgow City of Culture: Myths, politics and identity (Ashgate, 2007, forthcoming).

117 D Dorling and R Rees, 'A nation still dividing: the British census and social polarisation 1971–2001', Environment and Planning 35, 2003.

118 Quoted in Booker, Seven Basic Plots.

119 M Proust, Remembrance of Things Past (New York: Random House, 1934).

120 Hanlon et al Let Glasgow Flourish.

121 Glasgow Economic Forum, Step Change for Glasgow.

122 R Layard, Happiness: Lessons from a new science (London: Allen Lane, 2005).

123 A Offer, The Challenge of Affluence: Self control and well being in the United States and Britain since 1950 (Oxford: Oxford University Press, 2006).

124 R Florida and I Tinagli, Europe in the Creative Age (London: Demos, 2004).

125 RM Ryan and EL Deci, 'On happiness and human potentials: a review of research on hedonic and eudaimonic well-being', Annual Review of Psychology 52, 2001.

126 Y Benkler, 'Beyond state and market: social cooperation as a new domain of policy' in S Parker and N Gallagher (eds), The Collaborative State (Demos: London, 2007).

127 F Furedi, 'Save us from the politics of public behaviour', Spiked, 2006, see www.spiked-online.com/index.php?/site/article/1638/ (accessed 27 Apr 2007).

128 J Ogilvy, Creating Better Futures: Scenario planning as a tool for social creativity (New York: OUP, 2002).

129 J Ravetz, J Howe, C George and P Roberts, Environment and the City (London: Routledge, 1996).

130 From interviews that took place during workshops with Glasgow Housing Association tenants at a Glasgow 2020 story creation event on 7 June 2005.

131 This reflects a wider pattern of 'big stories' that have shaped human motivations over the past half-century, which as the Tomorrow Project set out fit together a bit like the layers of a Russian doll:
personal freedom: 1960s–70s – freedom

replaces Christianity as most people's personal story; emphasis on individual rights
personal authenticity: 1980s–90s – generation X was concerned with freedom to be self; using consumerism as a means of self-expression
personal happiness: 1990s–2000s – generation Y asked 'what is the goal of being authentic?' and answered 'a happy life'
personal improvement: 2000s–10s – self-development emerging as a way to structure and gain status in the happy life, augmented by new ways to self-improve physically and mentally, with new 'human enhancement' technology and drugs.
See: The Tomorrow Project, Individuals, Values and Identity, 2006, www.tomorrowproject.net/pub/1__glimpses/individuals__identity_and_values/-542.html (accessed 27 Apr 2007).

132 Y Benkler, *The Wealth of Networks: How social production transforms markets and freedom* (London: Yale University Press, 2006); C Leadbeater, *The Power of We-Think: The power of mass creativity*, (forthcoming but published online at www.wethinkthebook.net/home.aspx (accessed 7 May 2007).

133 D Topscott, AD Williams and A Sklar, *Wikinomics: How mass collaboration changes everything* (London: Portfolio, 2007).

134 Wikipedia, *Wikipedia: The free encyclopaedia*, see www.en.wikipedia.org/wiki/Wikipedia (accessed 22 Apr 2007).

135 RD Hof, 'The power of us: mass collaboration on the internet is shaking up business', *BusinessWeek*, 20 Jun 2005, see www.businessweek.com/magazine/content/05_25/b3938601.htm (accessed 27 Apr 2007).

136 Y Benkler, 'Beyond state and market: social cooperation as a new domain of policy' in N Gallagher and S Parker, *The Collaborative State* (London: Demos, 2007).

137 W Weaver, 'Science and complexity', *American Scientist* 36, 1948.

138 J Jacobs, *The Death and Life of Great American Cities* (New York: Random House, 1961).

139 See also P Skidmore, K Bound and H Lownsbrough, *Community Participation: Who benefits?* (London: Demos and Joseph Rowntree Foundation, 2006).

140 Topscott et al, *Wikinomics*.

141 A Steffen (ed), *Worldchanging: A user's guide for the 21st century* (New York: Abrams, 2006).

142 M Mean and C Tims, *People Make Places: Growing the public life of cities* (London: Demos, 2005).

143 For more information on the Huset Kulturcenter see www.huset-aarhus.dk/index_m1.html (accessed 1 May 2007).

144 Steffen, *Worldchanging*.

145 E Manzini and F Jegou, *Sustainable Everyday: Scenarios of everyday life* (Milan: Edizioni Ambiente, 2003).

146 For details of the 2007 Glasgow programme, see Glasgow Building Preservation Trust, www.gbpt.org/doorsopenday/index.html (accessed 22 Apr 2007).

147 The Equalities Review, *Fairness and Freedom: The final report of the Equalities Review* (London: Equalities Review, 2007).

148 H Gardner, *Five Minds for the Future* (Harvard: Harvard Business School Press, 2007).

149 K Sundquist, G Frank and J Sundquist, 'Urbanisation and incidence of psychosis and depression: follow-up study of 4.4 million women and men in Sweden', *British Journal of Psychiatry* 184 (2004).

150 Commission for Architecture and the Built Environment, *Housing Audit: Assessing the design quality of new housing in the East Midlands, West Midlands and the South West* (London: CABE, 2006).

151 S Hill, *Freiburg: The city with environmental and social sustainability at its heart*, Millennium Community Briefing Paper (London, 2005).

152 John Gilbert Architects, *Collree Self Build*, see www.johngilbert.co.uk/projects/newbuild/blair_self.html (accessed 22 Apr 2007).

153 J Barlow, R Jackson and J Meikle, *Homes to DIY for the UK's Self-Build Housing Market in the Twenty-First Century* (York: Joseph Rowntree, 2001).

154 Ibid.

155 G Leicester, *Rising to the Occasion: Cultural leadership in powerful times* (Bristol: Mission, Models, Money, 2007).

156 Hassan et al, *Scotland 2020*.

157 Mumford, *City in History*.

ABOUT DEMOS

Who we are
Demos is the think tank for everyday democracy.
We believe everyone should be able to make personal
choices in their daily lives that contribute to the common
good. Our aim is to put this democratic idea into
practice by working with organisations in ways that make
them more effective and legitimate.

What we work on
We focus on seven areas: public services; science
and technology; cities and public space; people and
communities; families and care; arts and culture; and
global security.

Who we work with
Our partners include policy-makers, companies, public
service providers and social entrepreneurs. Demos is not
linked to any party but we work with politicians across
political divides. Our international network — which
extends across Eastern Europe, Scandinavia, Australia,
Brazil, India and China — provides a global perspective
and enables us to work across borders.

How we work
Demos knows the importance of learning from
experience. We test and improve our ideas in practice
by working with people who can make change happen.
Our collaborative approach means that our partners
share in the creation and ownership of new ideas.

What we offer
We analyse social and political change, which we connect to innovation and learning in organisations. We help our partners show thought leadership and respond to emerging policy challenges.

How we communicate
As an independent voice, we can create debates that lead to real change. We use the media, public events, workshops and publications to communicate our ideas. All our books can be downloaded free from the Demos website.

www.demos.co.uk

DEMOS — Licence to Publish

1. **Definitions**

a "**Collective Work**" means a work, such as a periodical issue, anthology or encyclopedia, in which the Work in its entirety in unmodified form, along with a number of other contributions, constituting separate and independent works in themselves, are assembled into a collective whole. A work that constitutes a Collective Work will not be considered a Derivative Work (as defined below) for the purposes of this Licence.

b "**Derivative Work**" means a work based upon the Work or upon the Work and other pre-existing works, such as a musical arrangement, dramatization, fictionalization, motion picture version, sound recording, art reproduction, abridgment, condensation, or any other form in which the Work may be recast, transformed, or adapted, except that a work that constitutes a Collective Work or a translation from English into another language will not be considered a Derivative Work for the purpose of this Licence.

c "**Licensor**" means the individual or entity that offers the Work under the terms of this Licence.

d "**Original Author**" means the individual or entity who created the Work.

e "**Work**" means the copyrightable work of authorship offered under the terms of this Licence.

f "**You**" means an individual or entity exercising rights under this Licence who has not previously violated the terms of this Licence with respect to the Work, or who has received express permission from DEMOS to exercise rights under this Licence despite a previous violation.

2. **Fair Use Rights**. Nothing in this licence is intended to reduce, limit, or restrict any rights arising from fair use, first sale or other limitations on the exclusive rights of the copyright owner under copyright law or other applicable laws.

3. **Licence Grant**. Subject to the terms and conditions of this Licence, Licensor hereby grants You a worldwide, royalty-free, non-exclusive, perpetual (for the duration of the applicable copyright) licence to exercise the rights in the Work as stated below:

a to reproduce the Work, to incorporate the Work into one or more Collective Works, and to reproduce the Work as incorporated in the Collective Works;

b to distribute copies or phonorecords of, display publicly, perform publicly, and perform publicly by means of a digital audio transmission the Work including as incorporated in Collective Works; The above rights may be exercised in all media and formats whether now known or hereafter devised. The above rights include the right to make such modifications as are technically necessary to exercise the rights in other media and formats. All rights not expressly granted by Licensor are hereby reserved.

4. **Restrictions**. The licence granted in Section 3 above is expressly made subject to and limited by the following restrictions:

a You may distribute, publicly display, publicly perform, or publicly digitally perform the Work only under the terms of this Licence, and You must include a copy of, or the Uniform Resource Identifier for, this Licence with every copy or phonorecord of the Work You distribute, publicly display, publicly perform, or publicly digitally perform. You may not offer or impose any terms on the Work that alter or restrict the terms of this Licence or the recipients' exercise of the rights granted hereunder. You may not sublicence the Work. You must keep intact all notices that refer to this Licence and to the disclaimer of warranties. You may not distribute, publicly display, publicly perform, or publicly digitally perform the Work with any technological measures that control access or use of the Work in a manner inconsistent with the terms of this Licence Agreement. The above applies to the Work as incorporated in a Collective Work, but this does not require the Collective Work apart from the Work itself to be made subject to the terms of this Licence. If You create a Collective Work, upon notice from any Licencor You must, to the extent practicable, remove from the Collective Work any reference to such Licensor or the Original Author, as requested.

b You may not exercise any of the rights granted to You in Section 3 above in any manner that is primarily intended for or directed toward commercial advantage or private monetary compensation. The exchange of the Work for other copyrighted works by means of digital file-sharing or otherwise shall not be considered to be intended for or directed toward commercial advantage or private monetary compensation, provided there is no payment of any monetary compensation in connection with the exchange of copyrighted works.

If you distribute, publicly display, publicly perform, or publicly digitally perform the Work or any Collective Works, You must keep intact all copyright notices for the Work and give the Original Author credit reasonable to the medium or means You are utilizing by conveying the name (or pseudonym if applicable) of the Original Author if supplied; the title of the Work if supplied. Such credit may be implemented in any reasonable manner; provided, however, that in the case of a Collective Work, at a minimum such credit will appear where any other comparable authorship credit appears and in a manner at least as prominent as such other comparable authorship credit.

Representations, Warranties and Disclaimer

By offering the Work for public release under this Licence, Licensor represents and warrants that, to the best of Licensor's knowledge after reasonable inquiry:

Licensor has secured all rights in the Work necessary to grant the licence rights hereunder and to permit the lawful exercise of the rights granted hereunder without You having any obligation to pay any royalties, compulsory licence fees, residuals or any other payments;

The Work does not infringe the copyright, trademark, publicity rights, common law rights or any other right of any third party or constitute defamation, invasion of privacy or other tortious injury to any third party.

EXCEPT AS EXPRESSLY STATED IN THIS LICENCE OR OTHERWISE AGREED IN WRITING OR REQUIRED BY APPLICABLE LAW, THE WORK IS LICENCED ON AN "AS IS" BASIS, WITHOUT WARRANTIES OF ANY KIND, EITHER EXPRESS OR IMPLIED INCLUDING, WITHOUT LIMITATION, ANY WARRANTIES REGARDING THE CONTENTS OR ACCURACY OF THE WORK.

Limitation on Liability. EXCEPT TO THE EXTENT REQUIRED BY APPLICABLE LAW, AND EXCEPT FOR DAMAGES ARISING FROM LIABILITY TO A THIRD PARTY RESULTING FROM BREACH OF THE WARRANTIES IN SECTION 5, IN NO EVENT WILL LICENSOR BE LIABLE TO YOU ON ANY LEGAL THEORY FOR ANY SPECIAL, INCIDENTAL, CONSEQUENTIAL, PUNITIVE OR EXEMPLARY DAMAGES ARISING OUT OF THIS LICENCE OR THE USE OF THE WORK, EVEN IF LICENSOR HAS BEEN ADVISED OF THE POSSIBILITY OF SUCH DAMAGES.

7. **Termination**

a This Licence and the rights granted hereunder will terminate automatically upon any breach by You of the terms of this Licence. Individuals or entities who have received Collective Works from You under this Licence, however, will not have their licences terminated provided such individuals or entities remain in full compliance with those licences. Sections 1, 2, 5, 6, 7, and 8 will survive any termination of this Licence.

b Subject to the above terms and conditions, the licence granted here is perpetual (for the duration of the applicable copyright in the Work). Notwithstanding the above, Licensor reserves the right to release the Work under different licence terms or to stop distributing the Work at any time; provided, however that any such election will not serve to withdraw this Licence (or any other licence that has been, or is required to be, granted under the terms of this Licence), and this Licence will continue in full force and effect unless terminated as stated above.

8. **Miscellaneous**

a Each time You distribute or publicly digitally perform the Work or a Collective Work, DEMOS offers to the recipient a licence to the Work on the same terms and conditions as the licence granted to You under this Licence.

b If any provision of this Licence is invalid or unenforceable under applicable law, it shall not affect the validity or enforceability of the remainder of the terms of this Licence, and without further action by the parties to this agreement, such provision shall be reformed to the minimum extent necessary to make such provision valid and enforceable.

c No term or provision of this Licence shall be deemed waived and no breach consented to unless such waiver or consent shall be in writing and signed by the party to be charged with such waiver or consent.

d This Licence constitutes the entire agreement between the parties with respect to the Work licensed here. There are no understandings, agreements or representations with respect to the Work not specified here. Licensor shall not be bound by any additional provisions that may appear in any communication from You. This Licence may not be modified without the mutual written agreement of DEMOS and You.

I wish I could become a musician and help learn ¶ A Glasgow street Plaza ¶ Better skatepark higher and steeper ramps and freedom to skate anywhere ¶ I wish for Glasgow to be a cleaner city! ¶ I would like our local park to have more play facilities ¶ A cleaner, healthier, happier city ¶ More sun ¶ Glasgow to live, work and play together ¶ All children live in harmony ¶ All people happy together, no racism ¶ All races can live together in peace! Treat everyone with respect. ¶ No violence, racism or traffic ¶ The asylum-seekers allowed to stay and no racism ¶ No stabbings and no racism ¶ All people must live in peace! I suggest us to look at one another! Only love saves ¶ Graffiti free, litter free ¶ Better world ¶ All for everyone to be a cleaner city ¶ We wish for no racism ¶ No racism to be more tolerant, with behaviour that can bring the people together and root out racism ¶ A more tolerant society and a return to the friendly communities ¶ Children getting equal opportunities for the whole world ¶ I wish for Glasgow on all racism ¶ I would like big houses ¶ I would like everyone to play ¶ I wish that Glasgow would have more things to do in the world ¶ To have a community channel piped into every household ¶ Peace and integration between different nations ¶ An equal and selfless city to be envied by all ¶ I wish our schools would have no graffiti ¶ I wish for the fighting ¶ Better school activities, also all Glasgow city council activities are appreciated ¶ Healthy, more happiness and no racism ¶ Glasgow what I wish for the world ¶ Children would like helping hand extended to the whole world ¶ A more prosperous future ¶ I will contribute more actively to the local community and that more real investment. Children getting equal opportunities for a more prosperous future ¶ Healthy, clean open and friendly City for all! ¶ Clean ¶ a first and friendly helping hand extended to the whole world ¶ I wish for Glasgow to play ¶ I wish that Glasgow is a unique city ¶ I wish I was rich ¶ festivals like this continue to bring cultures of Glasgow together and more frequently ¶ I wish our schools and racism ¶ I wish I was financially happy with no debt ¶ I wish that Glasgow will be the place where I raise my grow up together as brothers and sisters regardless of their cultural backgrounds ¶ To be a safer city for all ¶ Clean Glasgow and work places ¶ I wish Glasgow can become playground ¶ being proud of their city ¶ cause it's great ¶ discriminating in schools and live in harmony. Crime free, less traffic, more trees ¶ Becca a Scoop lass 4eva!! Sal racism would stop ¶ Better school activities, also all Glasgow city council activities are appreciated ¶ I would like to work on recycling, better facilities. Glasgow and surrounding, when I am in Australia ¶ To have a Momina, Moshteg, Mohsin, Adz, Aisha, Azim, Nav, Desi Lot 4Eva stick together for life ¶ I wish the two best sisters in the world stick togeha all da time. N d sisterz called Monina + Moshena. So in ur face! ¶ To make life better ¶ More aquariums in Glasgow ¶ More horses in Glasgow city council to work on recycling, better integration for our future generations not only in black ethnic areas but More trees, less litter, people in Glasgow to be the cleaner, healthier less litter ¶ Be more environmentally aware. Glasgow city council to grow and prosper ¶ I wish Glasgow had more fun things to do. More free things ¶ A healthy, clean and harmonious city ¶ I want Glasgow to see football ¶ Be more quiet outside my flat KIDS! ¶ I had lots of money ¶ I wish the world no graffiti ¶ I wish the G-Hill massive crew Diya, outreach cultural events to other places than the main cities. People please integrate. Peace! ¶ There is only one race — the human race. We all need to start talking and working 2wards world peace 2020 Glasgow parliamentary debating association ¶ A healthy, clean, free of violence ¶ Less violence in schools ¶ I wish that Glasgow city council to grow and prosper. Thank-u ¶ I wish better integration for our future generations ¶ Bush, stop Blair. Start Talking ¶ I want Glasgow to see football ¶ I hope I'll be back in Scotland soon. I just love it! ¶ To have a council that cares about its staff and citizens ¶ Claire/Alana/Iceira/Clare Anastacia visit Clare in house. Clare get a dolphin x Alana go responsibly, being proud of their city. Don't destroy the old Glasgow ¶ Very very beautiful ¶ Healthy, clean, free of violence ¶ A healthy integrated, multicultural city to live in ¶ Tougher laws on anti-social behaviour longer jail terms for offenders, United we stand, divided we fall ¶ I wish Glasgow could cut dow anything, harmony across religions and ethnic groups would be dealt with care to raise us all ¶ I had lots of money ¶ I wish the world no graffiti ¶ Hoping and wishing I wish I was rich. The end ¶ I wish for a more cultured, bright and Ipod nano ¶ I wish to learn how community for everyone to share for those of us who have lost babies ¶ Clare/Alana/Iceira/Clare ¶ To visit glasgow again one day. First visit to Glasgow. Find to more multiculturally sensitive and with the love of all. It takes a city (village) to raise us all ¶ Peacefully ¶ Healthy, to be cleaner, healthier ¶ There is only one race — the human race ¶ Glasgow to hold the Commonwealth games in house ¶ I would like to see Glasgow on all children — safely and with the love of their city ¶ cause it's great ¶ Less violence in schools ¶ Simone ITG! ¶ Tougher laws, Naomi, Simone ITG! ¶ Glasgow to hold the Commonwealth games in 2020. I wish Glasgow could cut down children ¶ To make life better ¶ More aquariums in Glasgow ¶ Rebecca, Vayde, Naomi, Simone ITG! ¶ I wish I was rich ¶ I wish to come again with one another as equals, with no hatred or violence against each other. United we stand, divided we fall ¶ Peacefully and with the love of their city. Very very beautiful ¶ I wish that local Authorities. Glasgow. Why oh why is it that on a public or summer holiday time is ALWAYS when the council decide to put road work on the A82 whe Silver 4eva! Antonia 4 Boris. PNeeCVhris, Abdi 4eva hahaha! Oxo Antonia, Rebecca, Vayde, Naomi, Simone ITG! ¶ To have a council that cares about its staff and citizens ¶ I hope that Glasgow will stay this nice and beautiful forever. Love this place lots! ¶ I wish th the street 4eva ¶ Lowes Clare fancies ¶ I hope I'll be back in Scotland soon. I just love it! ¶ Glasgow has Commonwealth Games ¶ I wish I lived in a footballers house ¶ Freedom of speech is a basic human right. ¶ To visit glasgow for everyone to make it a better place to bring my two beautiful so McDees, Lowes Clare fancies ¶ Good luck ¶ Glasgow has Commonwealth Games ¶ I wish I lived in a footballers house ¶ Had a Lucky day. I wish for good health for all my family ¶ I wish for peace and happiness and Lot peoms to the Public advising on money sent as we should have awa weather like the weekend every day ¶ I wish my bum was smaller ¶ I wish we could come again with one another as equals, with no hatred or violence against each other. United we stand, divided we fall ¶ I would like to put road work on the Public advising on money sent as we should have awa + saw what a great thing this did for the city Good luck. Also help to poverty and ban all drugs even nicotine. ¶ Glasgow will come home again ¶ I wish to come home home again ¶ I wish for galleries and museums to live lives filled with health, happiness and end to war ¶ I wish I got everything I w I was scared forever. I love his piece of being ¶ Wish I could come to live with one another and ban all drugs even nicotine. ¶ Had also like to tackle their drug and knife poblems to remain accessible so that ever ¶ I wish to be a singer wh what we're lucky enough to get! I wish my brom ¶ Wish I could get my redundancy and get ot o there! ¶ Designern tomar a aquest iloc d'aqui moolts, molts anys pero' els dos junts!!! T'estimo albert ¶ I wish t knife crimes coz it's tearin' our streets apart. Also help to poverty and ban all drugs even nicotine. ¶ Had a Lucky day. I wish my grandchild will be a healthy cheerful baby ¶ I wish for a motorbike ¶ I wish to be a trampoline a council would allow the staff to have an opinion instead of being told what to do and what to say. Freedom of speech is a basic human right. ¶ I wish Scottish Independence ¶ I wish someone dug a trenc T'estimo Anna! I hope this place could be my second home and stays peace forever! ¶ all we Scots could come home home again ¶ I wish my grandchild will be a a healthy city at the forefront of good ideas ¶ I wish tha peacefully forever, I love his place could be my second home and stays peace forever after! ¶ I wish I didn't have to leave in two days ¶ I wish to have a future in art ¶ I wish the world to be free of terrorism and the wonderful place could be my second home and stays peace forever after! ¶ all we Scots could come home home again ¶ I wish my family ¶ I wish the world to be free of terrorism and the world ¶ I want Glasgow will fill with sunshine that Glasgow with sunshine ¶ Why are we selling off all our green belt land to construction of houses ¶ I hope I can pass all my exams and live happily in Glasgow. Oh ya, I hope Glasgow will be fr am older and my brother to be a football player ¶ I wish for a chance to do something creative and worthwhile. ¶ I wish I was rich so that I could give to the poor ¶ I wish England doesn't win the world cup ¶ I wish t milk with cornflakes ¶ I wish that Sloff and me live happily ever after! ¶ I wish West Dunbartonshire and Argyle and Bute would send letters to the Public advising on money ¶ I wish that could have without exception bring change or vandalism. ¶ I wish that Glasgow and surrounding and get got o there! ¶ Designern tomar a aquest iloc ¶ I wish the world was at peace with itself and stop slagging us off because we're different not global warming or vandalism. ¶ I wish the world to do and what to say. Freedom of speech is a basic human right ¶ I wish that Glasgow would get a life and stop slagging us off because we're different an artist when I grow up ¶ I wish for my children and their children to do something creative and worthwhile ¶ I wish to have a future in art ¶ I wish with all neds would get a life and stop slagging us off because we're different horse because I really like them loads. Also keep all the animals that could be extinct in art ¶ I wish for good health for all my family ¶ I wish to be an environmentally friendly city at the forefront of good ideas ¶ I wish that wh England will win the world cup ¶ I wish that England and it would be wrong (i.e. that England doesn't win the world cup) ¶ I wish for love everywhere ¶ I wish that John is wrong (i.e. that Tony Blair would stop telling us what to do ¶ I wish that wh between Scotland and England and it would give to the poor ¶ I wish that John is wrong (i.e. that Tony Blair would stop telling us what to do ¶ I wish that wh wish I would create a universe of my own ¶ I wish the world to leave in two days ¶ I wish to leave in two days (I.e. that Tony Blair would rethink their policies ¶ I wish Canada and the US wou want a pony ¶ I wish that home life for me and my friend would be an environmentally friendly city ¶ I wish for America and Britain to rethink their policies ¶ I wish for others in my hair ¶ May all who visit this S a horse and a thousand pounds ¶ I wish Glasgow would be an environmentally friendly city. It's my life ¶ I wish I was a punkrocker with flowers in my hair and still eat and drink what this p baby and get married ¶ I wish for me and my friend would be an environmentally friendly city ¶ I quote Bon Jovi. It's my life ¶ I wish I was a punkrocker with flowers in my hair ¶ I wish for an enjoyable S grow up I have a good job and a good house ¶ I wish I was a punkrocker ¶ I quote Bon Jovi. It's my life ¶ I wish I could lose weight and still eat and drink what this p and for America and Britain to rethink their policies ¶ I wish to stop, people stop s kinder to the planet ¶ I wish for others ¶ I wish for the fights to stop, people stop s healthy happy and full of love for others ¶ For all the people ¶ I wish for others ¶ I wish someone dug a trenc vacation for my family ¶ For all the people at the forefront of good ideas ¶ I wish that w drugs and clean streets. P.s. please god, anybody but ev Total destruction of the British class system ¶ Demo has clean rivers, and parks flourishing ¶ Hope C and cleaner, more environmentally friendly. Maybe one of my son sectarianism or big the radio. ¶ To have no Glasgow